The Canadian Practical Nurse Registration Examination PREP GUIDE

Fourth Edition

The clinical scenarios described in this prep guide are entirely fictional. No resemblance to real people or actual cases is intended.

Every effort was made to ensure the accuracy of the material presented in this prep guide at the time of publication.

Given that policies, procedures and instructions can change at any time, candidates should always read and follow directions provided by the regulatory authority, the presiding officer and the instructions contained in the Canadian Practical Nurse Registration Examination.

Candidates use the information, materials and suggestions in this prep guide at their own risk. Canada's Testing Company, Assessment Strategies Inc. assumes no responsibility for candidates' performance on the Canadian Practical Nurse Registration Examination.

ISBN 978-0-9781625-2-8. 4th edition 2011
(ISBN 0-9781625-0-1. 3rd edition 2006)
(ISBN 1-55119-998-X. 2nd edition 2001)
(ISBN 1-55119-123-7. 1st edition 1995)

Canada's Testing Company ™

Printed in Canada

September 2011

Table of Contents

Preface		iii
Acknowledgments		v
Chapter 1	Introduction	1
Chapter 2	Background on the CPNRE	7
Chapter 3	Exam Preparation and Test-Taking Strategies	15
Chapter 4	Taking the Practice Exam	25
Chapter 5	Scoring the Practice Exam	73
Chapter 6	Creating your Performance Profile	79
Chapter 7	Rationales for the Practice Exam	85
Chapter 8	CPNRE Predictor Test	135
Bibliography		143
Appendices		145
Appendix A	The CPNRE List of Competencies	145
Appendix B	Regulatory Authorities	151
Appendix C	Abbreviations used in the CPNRE and Practice Exam	153
Additional Materials		155
	Performance Profile Tally Sheets	155
	Performance Profile Chart	156
	Answer Sheets	157
	Satisfaction Survey	161

Preface

This 4th edition of *The Canadian Practical Nurse Registration Examination Prep Guide* was developed by Canada's Testing Company, Assessment Strategies Inc. (ASI), to help you prepare for the Canadian Practical Nurse Registration Examination (CPNRE). ASI is responsible for the development and administration of the CPNRE used by provincial and territorial regulatory authorities in Canada.

This prep guide is specifically designed to familiarize you with the latest competencies and practice questions of the CPNRE that will be introduced in January 2012. An interactive CD-ROM has once again been incorporated and includes the benefits of immediate feedback, creating a performance profile and focusing on specific competency categories. Also included is an added link to the CPNRE Predictor Test which is designed to help you gauge your readiness and to help you focus your studying by identifying your areas of strength and weakness. We believe that this prep guide, along with the Predictor Test, will help you enhance your nursing knowledge and test-taking strategies.

Over the years, ASI has used the advice and suggestions from students who have recently written the CPNRE as a basis for developing the prep guide. Practical nursing educators and practical nurses from across the country contributed to the development of the nursing situations and exam questions as well as the rationales for the correct answer and incorrect options and identified two current references for each question. An editorial review board ensured and verified that the questions and rationales are current and accurate.

To assist in improving this prep guide, we have included a customer satisfaction survey at the end. We would greatly appreciate receiving your valued comments and suggestions.

ASI would like to thank the many educators and practical nurses who collaborated with us to produce this 4th edition of *The Canadian Practical Nurse Registration Examination Prep Guide*. As a result of their efforts, we are confident that this prep guide will be of great assistance to you as you prepare to write the CPNRE.

Finally, our best wishes to you for success on the Canadian Practical Nurse Registration Examination and throughout your practical nursing career.

Canada's Testing Company, Assessment Strategies Inc.

Acknowledgments

The following people generously gave their time and expertise to the creation of *The Canadian Practical Nurse Registration Examination Prep Guide* (4th ed.).

Exam Review Panel

This panel consisted of practical nurses, practical nurse educators and administrators from different locations and work settings in Canada. They reviewed the content of the Practice Exam and rationales, independently and as a group to ensure the quality of these important prep guide components.

CPNRE Prep Guide Committee

Frances Abbott, *Newfoundland*
Patricia Chornaby, *Ontario*
Hélène Desjardins, *Ontario*
Marla Fraser, *Saskatchewan*
Laura Kowalsky, *Alberta*
Chantal Morin, *Ontario*
Mary Lou Nicholson, *New Brunswick*
Catherine Overton, *British Columbia*
Marie-France Roy, *Nouveau-Brunswick*

Item Mapping Committee

Denice Evanishin, *British Columbia*
Kelly Fleming, *Alberta*
Paula Gauthier, *Prince Edward Island*
Deborah Pelham O'Brien, *New Brunswick*

Item Writers

Hundreds of practical nurses, practical nurse educators and administrators from across Canada participated in item-writing sessions at which the questions and rationales were developed for use on the Practice Exam. Although they are too numerous to name individually, ASI wishes to thank these individuals for their time, skills and dedication.

ASI Staff Contributors

A team of ASI staff members contributed to the creation and development of the prep guide and CD-ROM. Some were responsible for writing content and incorporating it into the prep guide as well as the planning and managing of activities related to the design and layout.

Chris Beauchamp, *Senior Consultant*
Christine Erin Logue, *Project Administrator*
Murielle Lalonde, *Translation Coordinator*
Kristy Brandon-Smith, *Project Administrator*
Rachel Buttle, *Manager, Testing Services*

1

Introduction 1

Introduction

The Canadian Practical Nurse Registration Examination Prep Guide (4th ed.) was developed by Canada's Testing Company, Assessment Strategies Inc. (ASI). The purpose of the prep guide is to assist candidates who will be writing the Canadian Practical Nurse Registration Examination (CPNRE). The fourth edition of the prep guide is designed specifically for those candidates who plan to write the CPNRE in January 2012 or later. The CPNRE is offered as a paper-and-pencil exam.

In order to enhance your learning experience, we have also reproduced the Practice Exam questions on a CD-ROM with this fourth edition of the prep guide. You can choose between two approaches. One approach, known as *testing mode*, allows you to take the Practice Exam under the same conditions as the actual exam. The other approach, referred to as *feedback mode*, allows you to receive immediate feedback following your response to a question. Both approaches provide you with a summary of your overall performance at the end of your practice session.

Success on the CPNRE depends on two main factors: (1) your knowledge of practical nursing principles and content; and (2) your ability to apply this knowledge in the context of specific health-care scenarios presented on the CPNRE.

This prep guide can help you in both areas. Completing the prep guide Practice Exam will help you review and integrate the concepts you have learned in your practical nursing program. It will also help you assess your skill in applying that knowledge. The Practice Exam instructions, test-taking strategies, question rationales and sample answer sheets within the prep guide can be used to enhance your readiness to write the CPNRE. The CD-ROM should also prove beneficial. What better way to get ready than to gain practical experience by trying the practice questions in the prep guide and knowing what to expect on the CPNRE.

The prep guide consists of eight chapters designed to help you with different aspects of your preparation. In this chapter, you will learn the best way to use the prep guide and the CD-ROM given your individual needs and the amount of time you have to prepare for the CPNRE. Chapter 2 provides you with background information on the development, organization and format of the CPNRE. Information is also presented on the prevention and detection of cheating on the CPNRE. Chapter 3 contains a variety of general test-taking strategies, as well as specific strategies for answering multiple-choice questions. The Practice Exam is presented in Chapter 4 as well as on the CD-ROM. Chapter 5 explains how to use the answer key to score the Practice Exam and describes how the actual CPNRE is scored.

After checking your score on the Practice Exam against a score interpretation scale, you may wish to develop a Performance Profile; a self-evaluation of your strengths and weaknesses. Chapter 6 shows you how to create your Performance Profile. This profile is created automatically when you take the Practice Exam on the CD-ROM. The rationales for each option in the Practice Exam are found in Chapter 7 and are presented to you when you work with the CD-ROM in the *feedback mode*. Finally, in Chapter 8, important information on the CPNRE online Predictor Test is presented.

The Bibliography lists all of the references cited in the question rationales. Appendix A presents the competencies that make up the content domain for the CPNRE. Addresses of the provincial and territorial regulatory authorities are provided in Appendix B, and Appendix C contains a list of common abbreviations that appear on the CPNRE and the Practice Exam. At the end of the prep guide, you will find two blank answer sheets for the Practice Exam, a blank tally sheet to create your Performance Profile and a Satisfaction Survey. Your opinion is important to us and we encourage you to send us your feedback to help us improve future editions of *The Canadian Practical Nurse Registration Examination Prep Guide*.

Finally, inside the back cover, your copy of the CD-ROM is enclosed.

Before you begin...

The prep guide is designed to familiarize you with the format of the actual exam and to provide you with information on the content of the exam. The Practice Exam contained in this prep guide, and also on the CD-ROM, is a simulation of the actual CPNRE. The Practice Exam contains 180 questions.

The questions presented in the Practice Exam are typical of those you will see on the CPNRE. They represent common and predictable health situations of the population in those contexts or environments where entry-level practical nurses would work in a generalist role. As with the actual CPNRE, the questions on the Practice Exam have been developed and reviewed by reviewed by practical nurses, practical nurse educators and administrators who represent a variety of nursing programs, different clinical backgrounds and different regions of the country. Furthermore, the Practice Exam has been designed according to the specifications and guidelines outlined in the *Canadian Practical Nurse Registration Examination Blueprint* (2012), the document used to construct the actual CPNRE. Although the Practice Exam is not identical to the CPNRE that you will write, both exams contain questions that measure the specific competencies expected of practical nurses beginning to practise.

One of the most important features of the prep guide is that, for each question on the Practice Exam, rationales are provided to explain why the options are correct or incorrect. These rationales emphasize nursing concepts and principles that are essential for entry-level practical nurses. For example, although the assessment questions on the prep guide Practice Exam are different from those on the actual exam, the general principles and concepts being tested are the same because the questions are developed from the same set of competencies. Thus, by using the Practice Exam to review and reinforce the principles of client assessment, you will be better prepared to answer these types of questions on the CPNRE.

It is important to note that, although your score on the Practice Exam can give you some indication of how prepared you are for the CPNRE, the prep guide is only one aid to promoting your success. The prep guide should be used to supplement and consolidate the knowledge and skills taught in your educational program.

Each question on the prep guide Practice Exam is supported by two references. Most of these references have been published within the past five years. The purpose of the references is twofold: (1) to indicate that the correct answer within each question has authoritative support from at least two experts in the field and (2) to provide you with a source for further reading and review. Every attempt has been made to use references that are up-to-date, accessible and accepted within the nursing community. If you are unable to locate the specific references cited in the Bibliography, there are many other equally sound nursing texts that provide support for the questions in the Practice Exam.

Methods of using the prep guide

The prep guide, including the CD-ROM, can be used in different ways depending on your particular needs and the amount of time you have before you write the CPNRE. The three methods suggested below are not independent, but can actually be used successively as part of a comprehensive study plan. Each method should be preceded by a review of Chapters 1, 2 and 3 before advancing to Chapter 4, *Taking the Practice Exam*, or using the CD-ROM. The three methods differ in approach based on the amount of time you have available before you write the CPNRE. They cover periods of several months prior, one month prior and two weeks prior to the actual exam.

Method A: Several months before writing the CPNRE

If you have several months before the exam, you may wish to write the complete Practice Exam under conditions that do not simulate the actual exam (e.g., do not be concerned with time limits; look ahead to a rationale to understand why a given option is correct or incorrect before choosing your answer). Consider this process as a "dry run" to familiarize yourself with the prep guide and the format and layout of the exam. In using this approach, work question-by-question without using the answer sheets. Answer one question and immediately check to see if you selected the correct answer. Then read the rationales for the correct answer and the incorrect options to gain insight into what made you answer correctly or incorrectly.

On the CD-ROM, this would correspond to the *feedback mode* where you receive immediate feedback on whether you responded correctly or incorrectly, and why. If you repeat a session in *feedback mode*, the order of the exam questions will be randomized each time.

This method will give you hands-on experience with multiple-choice questions and will help you identify any difficulties you may have with the multiple-choice format (e.g., failing to focus on key words in the question, making unwarranted assumptions and reading too much into questions). In Chapter 3, you will find a checklist of common test-taking errors that may help you determine if you have particular difficulties with multiple-choice questions that you can correct before writing the exam.

Since this method does not simulate actual exam conditions, we recommend that you do not calculate your total score or make any inferences based on how well you perform.

Method B: One month before writing the CPNRE

If you have approximately one month before the exam, you will want to more closely simulate actual exam conditions and still take advantage of a considerable amount of time in which to address any self-diagnosed weaknesses. To use this method, complete the Practice Exam, either in its entirety or in separate sections (e.g., a set of cases or a set of independent questions) before checking your answers against the answer key. Next, calculate your total score and interpret it according to the guidelines provided in Chapter 5. Then develop your Performance Profile (see Chapter 6) to identify your strengths and weaknesses.

1

The results of this self-diagnosis can then be used to identify gaps or deficiencies in your knowledge and skills. By knowing that you are weak in particular competency categories, for example, you can make your remaining study time more productive by concentrating on those specific areas. Studying for the CPNRE will also be made easier by consulting the reference books linked to specific nursing topics. You will find these references cited in the rationales for each question and listed in full in the Bibliography.

If you use the CD-ROM version of the Practice Exam, you would take the exam in *testing mode*. However, you would not necessarily respect the time limits of the actual exam.

Method C: Two weeks before writing the CPNRE

Method C is based upon a complete simulation of the actual exam. Follow the Practice Exam instructions precisely, time yourself and use the answer sheets as if you were actually writing the CPNRE. You can still benefit from creating your Performance Profile as suggested in Method B. For the remaining study time, it may be most useful for you to concentrate on specific areas in which any weaknesses were identified. When using Method C, if you do not have time to obtain the references that correspond to your areas of weakness, you may prefer to concentrate on the rationales provided for each question in the Practice Exam. Applying Method C on the CD-ROM corresponds to *testing mode*. Here, as in the paper-and-pencil approach, you would respect all the exam administration guidelines (time limits, no reference materials, etc.). Your result and a Performance Profile will be generated automatically when you have completed the entire Practice Exam in *testing mode*.

2

2 Background on the CPNRE

Background on the CPNRE

Each Canadian provincial and territorial regulatory authority for practical nurses is responsible for ensuring that all entry-level practical nurses[1] within its jurisdiction meet an acceptable level of competence before they begin to practise. This level of competence is measured partly by the CPNRE administered by all provincial and territorial regulatory authorities[2] (except in Quebec).This ensures a common standard that all practical nurses practicing in these jurisdictions must meet.

Canada's Testing Company, Assessment Strategies Inc. has been developing the CPNRE since 1971. The exam, offered in English and French, has always been comprehensive in nature (i.e., integrating all clinical areas, such as obstetrics, pediatrics, etc.). The content and format of the exam, however, have been adapted over the years to meet the changing requirements for licensure / registration as a practical nurse in Canada. The first administration of the newest version of the CPNRE will take place in January 2012.

The process used to develop the CPNRE is referred to as a criterion-referenced (C-R) approach. With the C-R approach, the CPNRE is developed to measure an explicitly defined content domain which consists of the competencies expected of entry-level practical nurses. In 2009-2010, a thorough review and updating of these competencies resulted in a new set of competencies which forms the basis of the January 2012 and later versions of the CPNRE. These new competencies, and the guidelines and specifications that outline the way they are measured on the exam, are presented in the ASI publication *Canadian Practical Nurse Registration Examination Blueprint* (2012).

As with the previous exams, the new version of the CPNRE is the end result of many exam development activities that take place throughout a two-year period. Practical nurse educators, clinicians and administrators from across Canada create and evaluate exam questions with assistance from ASI test consultants, who ensure that the CPNRE meets the Blueprint guidelines and specifications.

What is tested with the CPNRE

As mentioned above, the content and specifications for the CPNRE are described in the Blueprint. A Summary Chart that outlines the Blueprint specifications for exam development is presented at the end of this chapter for your reference. In Appendix A, you will find the complete list of 84 competencies that make up the content domain for the CPNRE. Each question on the CPNRE is linked to one of these competencies. The sections below provide brief explanations of the variables and guidelines referred to in the Summary Chart.

1 For the purposes of this document, the term "practical nurse" represents both licensed practical nurses and registered practical nurses.
2 The regulatory authorities impose eligibility criteria, such as the completion of an approved practical nursing educational program, which provide the added information required to decide on an individual's readiness to practise safely and effectively.

Competency Framework

A framework was developed to identify and organize the competencies that the CPNRE will assess. The framework and definitions of the three framework categories are presented later. The number of competencies in each category is indicated in parentheses following the category name. The number of competencies in each category is not necessarily reflective of the importance each category has in the practice of practical nursing.

2

- Professional, ethical and legal practice (27 competencies)
- Foundations of practice (43 competencies)
- Collaborative practice (14 competencies)

Competencies

This first section of the Summary Chart of Development Guidelines for the Canadian Practical Nurse Registration Examination shows that the set of competencies has been organized into three broad categories: (1) Professional, ethical and legal practice (20-30%); (2) Foundations of practice (55-65%); and (3) Collaborative practice (10-20%).

Professional, Ethical and Legal Practice

The practical nurse is responsible for providing safe, competent and ethical nursing care while developing and maintaining a therapeutic nurse-client relationship. A code of ethics provides direction for the practical nurse to uphold the highest standard of care as defined by the scope of practice. The practical nurse maintains autonomy and is legally accountable to the client, the employer and the profession.

Foundations of Practice

As a member of the health-care team, the practical nurse is integral in the assessment, planning, implementation, evaluation and documentation of nursing care. The practical nurse promotes, supports and advocates for client self-determination to achieve optimum health outcomes. The practical nurse uses critical thinking to guide the formulation of clinical decisions, based on evidence-informed practice.

Collaborative Practice

The practical nurse works collaboratively with other members of the health-care team while maintaining autonomy within scope of practice. The practical nurse develops and maintains a therapeutic nurse-client relationship. The practical nurse demonstrates leadership while fostering continued growth of self and others to meet the challenges of the evolving health-care system.

In addition, the set of competencies is broken into two groups, with each group receiving a different weight on the CPNRE. The two groups were formed on the basis of a competency validation survey in which practical nurses, practical nurse educators and administrators across Canada rated the competencies according to importance and frequency. The weights associated with these groups have been assigned to reflect the relative importance and frequency of the competencies in each group. Thus, 48 competencies have been identified as being *very important* and comprise 55-65% of the CPNRE. The 36 remaining competencies have been identified as being *important* and comprise 35-45% of the CPNRE.

Structural Variables

Structural variables include those characteristics that determine the general design and appearance of the exam. They define the length of the exam, the format for establishing and maintaining the standard, the format/presentation of the exam questions (i.e., multiple-choice format) and special functions of exam questions (e.g., to measure a competency within the cognitive domain).

Exam length

The CPNRE consists of between 180 and 200 objective multiple-choice questions. An exam of 180 to 200 multiple-choice questions is sufficient to make both reliable and valid decisions about a practical nurse's readiness to practise safely, effectively and ethically.

Test equating

Once an acceptable standard has been determined on a form of the exam, a statistical procedure can be performed to establish a corresponding standard on subsequent forms of the exam. This procedure, known as test equating, takes into account the difficulty of the set of questions on the original and subsequent forms as well as any differences that exist in candidate performance. The pass mark of the original form is then carried forward and adjusted to reflect the differences in content difficulty and candidate performance on the new form of the exam. This statistical procedure ensures that all candidates, regardless of which test form they write, must achieve an equivalent standard to successfully pass the exam.

Question presentation and format

The multiple-choice questions are presented either within a case-based scenario or as independent questions.

The case-based format consists of a set of approximately three to five questions that are associated with a brief health-care scenario. Independent questions are stand-alone questions that contain all the necessary information without reference to a case. For the 180-200 questions on the CPNRE, 55-75% are presented as independent questions and 25-45% are presented within cases.

Cognitive Levels

Questions on the CPNRE measure candidates' competencies in practical nursing contexts across different levels of the cognitive domain. The three levels of ability reflected in the CPNRE are Knowledge/Comprehension, Application and Critical Thinking. The cognitive levels are defined below.

Knowledge/Comprehension

This level combines the ability to recall previously learned material and to understand its meaning. It includes such mental abilities as knowing and understanding definitions, facts and principles, and interpreting data (e.g., knowing the effects of certain procedures or interventions, understanding a change in a client's vital signs). Knowledge/comprehension questions make up a maximum of 15% of the CPNRE.

Application

This level refers to the ability to apply knowledge and learning to new or practical situations. It includes applying rules, methods, principles and nursing theories in providing care to clients (e.g., applying principles of drug administration and concepts of comfort and safety to the nursing care of clients). A minimum of 50% of the questions on the CPNRE are at the application level.

Critical Thinking

The third level deals with higher-level thinking processes. It includes the ability to judge the relevance of data, to deal with abstractions and to solve problems (e.g., identifying priorities of care, evaluating the effectiveness of nursing actions). The practical nurse should be able to identify cause-and-effect relationships, distinguish between relevant and irrelevant data, formulate valid conclusions and make judgments concerning the needs of clients. The critical thinking level of the cognitive domain represents a minimum of 35% of the questions on the CPNRE.

Contextual Variables

Contextual variables qualify the content domain by specifying the nursing contexts in which the exam questions will be set (e.g., client type, age of the individual client, client diversity and work environment).

Client type

For the purpose of the CPNRE, the client refers to individuals (or their designated representative), families and groups.

Client age

The use of the client age variable ensures that the individual clients described in the exam represent the demographic characteristics of the population encountered by the entry-level practical nurse. Available statistics (e.g., Canadian hospital separations by age and gender, and Canadian population by age and gender) were used to determine specifications for these variables.

Client diversity

Questions will be included that measure awareness, sensitivity and respect for diversity, without introducing stereotypes.

Work environment

Practical nurses work in a variety of practice settings and contexts where health care is delivered. As a result, the work environment is *only* specified where necessary.

How the CPNRE is Organized

The CPNRE is presented in one Test Book that is written over a four-hour period.

Each question on the exam, whether in the case or independent format, contains a stem and four options. The stem is typically made up of one to three sentences that provide relevant information or data and the specific practical nursing question that is being asked. Of the four options, one is the correct (or best) answer and the remaining three are incorrect (or less correct) options.

Some of the questions in each Test Book are *experimental*. That is, they are administered experimentally to determine their suitability for use on future exams. Although your answers to these experimental questions do not count toward your score, it is important to do your best on each question on the exam because you will have no way of knowing which questions are experimental.

You will find examples of the type of questions used in the actual CPNRE in Chapter 4, *Taking the Practice Exam*.

Summary Chart: Development Guidelines

Competencies			
Competency framework categories and weightings	Professional, ethical and legal practice:		20-30%
	Foundations of practice:		55-65%
	Collaborative practice:		10-20%
Structural Variables			
Exam length	Total:		180-200 questions
Test equating	Anchor questions are used to accomplish test equating.		
Question format and presentation	Format:		Multiple choice
	Presentation:		Independent questions - 55-75%
			Case-based questions - 25-45%
Cognitive levels	Knowledge/Comprehension:		Maximum of 15%
	Application:		Minimum of 50%
	Critical Thinking:		Minimum of 35%
Contextual Variables			
Client age	Age range	Group description	Target percentage
	0-18 years	Neonate to adolescent	10-20%
	19-69 years	Adult	50-60%
	70+ years	Older adult	20-30%
	Exam questions will reflect health situations relevant to all phases of life.		
Client diversity	Questions will be included that measure awareness, sensitivity and respect for diversity, without introducing stereotypes.		
Work environment	Practical nurses work in a variety of practice settings and contexts where health care is delivered. As a result, the work environment is *only* specified where necessary.		

3

Exam Preparation and Test-Taking Strategies

3

Exam Preparation and Test-Taking Strategies

This chapter will help you prepare to write the CPNRE by reviewing what you need to do before and during the exam, what to bring to the exam centre and how you can best perform on multiple-choice questions.

Before the CPNRE

Arrange to Write the CPNRE

To write the CPNRE, you must arrange to do so by contacting the regulatory authority in the province or territory in which you wish to write. The regulatory authority's staff will inform you of the documentation you must provide to register for the exam as well as the fee you will have to pay. A list of regulatory authorities that use the CPNRE can be found in Appendix B.

All candidates are entitled to receive a fair and valid assessment. To this end, the regulatory authorities, in conjunction with ASI, will authorize reasonable and appropriate modifications to the CPNRE administration procedures to accommodate candidates with disabilities. For further information, contact the regulatory authority in your jurisdiction.

Read the *CPNRE Prep Guide*

This prep guide, including the CD-ROM, contains information that will help you become more familiar with the CPNRE. The rationales for the correct answers (and the incorrect options) and the references listed in the Bibliography provide an ideal way to review essential nursing content. You are also presented with a variety of ways to use the prep guide and CD-ROM, depending on how much time you have before you write the CPNRE.

Take the Practice Exam in the prep guide

Taking the Practice Exam under conditions that are as close as possible to those of the actual exam is an ideal way to prepare and to ensure that there will be no surprises. Give yourself the right amount of time to complete the Practice Exam and do not look ahead to the answers.

Use the information from your Performance Profile

By conducting an analysis of your performance on the Practice Exam, you will be able to identify your strengths and weaknesses. Use this information to focus your studying in areas of weakness. If you are taking the paper-and-pencil version of the exam, use the information on how to create your Performance Profile found in Chapter 6. With the CD-ROM version, your Performance Profile is generated automatically.

Study effectively

Select a place for studying that is quiet, comfortable and free from distractions. Develop a study plan schedule, dividing your time between specific topics or sections. Keep in mind that five 2-hour sessions are likely to be more beneficial than two 5-hour periods. Monitor your progress and revise your schedule as necessary.

Predictor Tests

Consider using the Predictor Tests to assess your current level of preparation. There are two Predictor Tests that contain 100 separate questions each. These questions are similar to those found on the CPNRE. More information on the Predictor Tests can be found in a later chapter.

Prepare for the exam day

Check the location of the exam centre and exam room and determine how much time you will need to get there. If necessary, do a practice run and confirm bus schedules or the availability of parking. As well, it is important to be alert and focused when you write the exam. Be sure to get plenty of rest and to eat a suitable breakfast before you arrive at the exam centre.

What to Bring to the CPNRE

Identification

You are required to bring a current government-issued photo ID (e.g., driver's license, passport, military ID). The first and last name printed on the photo ID must match exactly the first and last name submitted to the regulatory authority on the CPNRE application.

Candidate exam identification card with bar code labels

In most cases, you must bring your candidate exam identification card with bar code labels issued by your CPNRE regulatory authority.

Pencils/eraser

Unless otherwise advised, bring two or three medium-soft (HB) sharpened pencils and a soft pencil eraser.

Personal items

The personal items listed below are permitted at your desk. They must be placed in a small, clear plastic bag and be visible during the admission to the exam room. All other personal items must be stored in a designated area in or outside of the exam room.

- one small, clear water bottle (500 mL) with no label
- throat lozenges only
- clear plastic package of tissues
- foam/non-electronic ear plugs and
- analog watch

The personal items listed below may be brought into the exam room, but **may not be placed near your desk area**.

- bags (e.g., backpacks, knapsacks, briefcase, tote bags, etc.)
- feminine hygiene products
- purses and wallets
- coats and jackets
- gloves and scarves

Important: You will be required to leave such items in a designated area inside or outside of the room. The regulatory authorities and ASI are not responsible for the security of any personal items brought to the writing centres.

What to wear

Remember that you will be sitting for hours. Wear comfortable, layered clothing that can be adjusted to the room's temperature. Sweaters may not have pockets or a hood. Please wear soft-soled shoes to maintain a quiet exam environment.

What Not to Bring

The following items are strictly prohibited in the exam room:

- Any electronic or communication devices, including but not limited to:
  - cellular/mobile phones
  - Ipods/tablet computers
  - hand-held computers
  - calculators
  - pagers
  - cameras of any kind
  - personal digital assistants (PDA)
  - digital watches
  - headphones/headsets/earpieces
  - music equipment
  - recording devices
- Study materials of any kind, including but not limited to:
  - books
  - notes
  - blank paper
- Hats of any kind, including but not limited to:
  - baseball caps
  - tuque (knitted cap)
  - hooded sweater/jacket
- Food or drink, including candy and gum (however the candidate is allowed one small clear water bottle [500 mL] with no label)
- Pens of any kind (ink, ballpoint, digital, mechanical pens/erasers)
- Scents (e.g., perfume, lotion, cologne, aftershave). To respect those who are sensitive to scents, the exam room is a scent-free environment.

Special Requests

If you have a disability prohibiting you from taking the exam under the conditions stated above or a special request such as a medical need (e.g., hearing aid, medication, asthma pump, etc.), you must receive advance approval by the regulatory authority during the application process to allow special items in the exam room on exam day.

During the CPNRE

Listen to all announcements

The presiding officer will inform you of important details, such as how long you have to complete the exam and where to hand in your exam Test Book and answer sheet.

Read the Test Book instructions

Exam instructions are very important. It is essential that you have a clear understanding of what you are expected to do. If you don't understand what you have been told or what you have read, ask questions in the period before the exam officially begins.

Complete all information accurately

You will be required to complete certain information on your answer sheet and Test Book (e.g., your candidate number from your identification card). Errors made in completing this information can delay the scoring of your exam. And if you make errors in recording your choice of answers, you will not be given any credit. Be sure that for each question you have recorded a single answer in the appropriate place on the answer sheet.

Answering multiple-choice questions

Consider each question separately. Try not to rush, but do not spend more than 1 to 1½ minutes on any question. If you do not know the answer to a question, skip it and return to it later. If you still do not know the correct answer, you can make a guess.

If you do not answer all of the multiple-choice questions in sequence, make sure that the oval you are filling in on your answer sheet is aligned with the correct question number.

When you decide on a correct answer, mark your choice on the answer sheet before moving on to the next question. Do not circle all the answers in the Test Book and then transfer them to the answer sheet because you could run out of time. Credit is not given for answers in your Test Book, only for answers recorded on your answer sheet.

Changing your answer

If you decide to change an answer after filling it in on your answer sheet, make sure the original choice is completely erased. Otherwise, it will appear as though you have selected two options. This will be scored as a wrong answer. Similarly, avoid making stray marks on your answer sheet that the computer could inadvertently pick up as answers to questions.

Be cautious about changing your answer. Very often your first choice is correct. Making a new selection is only advantageous if you are confident that the new choice is correct.

Read the question carefully

Concentrate on what is being asked in the question and relate this to the data provided. Do not make any assumptions unless they are directly implied.

Pick out *important* words that relate to the question. For example, in some questions you may be asked for the most appropriate *initial* response by the practical nurse; other questions may deal with the practical nurse's most *ethical* response or the practical nurse's most *therapeutic* response. Reviewing the questions in the Practice Exam will help you to recognize key words that will appear on the CPNRE.

Guessing

There is no penalty for guessing on the CPNRE. You will not lose any marks if you select an incorrect answer.

Strategies for Multiple-Choice Questions

Familiarize Yourself with Multiple-Choice Questions

A thorough understanding of multiple-choice questions will allow you to most effectively apply your knowledge and skills to the testing situation.

A multiple-choice question is constructed so that only someone who has mastered the subject matter will select the correct answer; to that person, only one option will appear to be the correct answer. To someone who lacks a firm grasp of the subject matter, all options may look plausible.

Use a three-step approach

It is often helpful to use the following three-step approach to answer the multiple-choice questions that appear on the CPNRE.

1. Carefully read the information provided in the case text (for cases) and in the stem of the question. Try to understand the client's health situation and the care the client is likely to require.
2. Read the stem carefully. Before looking at the options, make sure you have understood the question. Use the information provided and, based on your knowledge and skills, try to anticipate the correct answer.
3. Study the alternatives provided and select the one that comes closest to the answer you predicted. You may wish to reread the stem before finalizing your selection.

Take advantage of the process of elimination

If you are not presented with an option that matches, or is close to, the one you predicted after reading the stem, try to eliminate some of the options that are clearly incorrect.

The following example illustrates how you can benefit from the process of elimination.

Question

Which response by the practical nurse would best assist Mrs. Clement to verbalize her fears when she expresses anxiety about the possibility of having a mastectomy?

1. "I know exactly how you feel about this."
2. "Would you like to talk to the nurse-in-charge?"
3. "You seem worried that you may need to have surgery."
4. "It's a normal reaction to be afraid when faced with surgery."

To take full advantage of the process of elimination, it is important to focus on the key idea in the stem. The key idea is assisting the client to verbalize her fears.

In Option 1, the focus is on the practical nurse and not on the client or her concerns. Option 1 can be eliminated because it is highly unlikely that any one person knows exactly how someone else feels in a given situation.

Option 2 also fails to address the client's immediate concern because the practical nurse completely avoids dealing with the client and passes the responsibility on to another team member. For this reason, Option 2 can be eliminated as a possible correct answer.

Option 4 should be eliminated immediately. By telling the client that what she is experiencing is "normal," the practical nurse implies that the client's situation is routine. Such a response would be depersonalizing and non-therapeutic.

After these three options are systematically eliminated, you can consider Option 3, the correct option, which is an open-ended response that encourages the client to begin talking about how she feels about her upcoming surgery.

Checklist of common test-taking errors

Candidates often make mistakes on an exam because of errors in processing facts and information or because of difficulties with multiple-choice questions. These are technical errors related more to writing exams than to a lack of knowledge or skill.

As you proceed through the Practice Exam and determine whether you answered questions correctly, you may wish to keep a checklist of problems you had related to your test-taking skills. You can then use the results of this checklist to identify skills that you need to develop during your preparation for the CPNRE.

A checklist of common test-taking errors is provided below. Check off the particular technical error(s) you made with the questions you answered incorrectly. Keep in mind that you may have more than one technical error with any one question.

Checklist of Common Test-Taking Errors

- ☐ Missed important information in the case text
- ☐ Misread the stem of the question
- ☐ Failed to pick out important or key words in the stem of the question
- ☐ Did not relate the question to information in the case text
- ☐ Made assumptions in the case text or question
- ☐ Focused on insignificant details and missed key issues
- ☐ Selected more than one answer
- ☐ Incorrectly transferred answer from selection in test book to answer sheet
- ☐ Changed original answer
- ☐ Other (specify) ____

____

____

Cheating on the CPNRE

While most CPNRE candidates are ethical and professional, cheating unfortunately is on the rise.

Prior to Exam Day

Prior to the exam day, you will be sent information as to what you can and cannot bring to the exam room. Please know these rules and follow them. Check with your regulatory authority for details.

Exam Day

On exam day, you will be required to sign a "candidate declaration" agreeing not to engage in cheating behaviour. Below is a replica of what you must read and sign before writing the exam.

Important notice

This Test Book and its contents, including the exam questions, are highly confidential and are the property of Canada's Testing Company, Assessment Strategies Inc. (ASI). Candidates taking the exam are therefore prohibited, during or after the examination, from disclosing the contents of the Test Book and must not, under any circumstances, share any of the information it contains with any person, except as authorized by ASI. Unauthorized production, reproduction or publication of the exam questions is also prohibited by copyright laws. In addition, ASI has implemented measures and statistical procedures to detect cheating (i.e., copying answers from another candidate; voluntarily or involuntarily providing answers to another candidate). Unauthorized disclosure of the contents of the Test Book and any other form of cheating is unethical behaviour and shall result in sanctions. If the regulatory authority determines a candidate has cheated on the exam, the candidate is automatically assigned a fail result and the writing is counted as an exam writing. Other sanctions may be imposed and may extend to being denied access into the profession.

Candidate declaration

I acknowledge that I have read the above provisions regarding the disclosure, production, reproduction or publication of the Test Book and its content, and cheating with respect to the exam. My signature on this Test Book constitutes my agreement not to disclose, produce, reproduce or otherwise engage in the publication of the Test Book and its content, unless authorized by ASI, or to cheat with respect to the exam.

____

[your signature]

Data Forensics

After you write the exam, routine data forensics procedures are conducted on every candidate. Your answer sheet and everyone else's answer sheet is screened for suspicious response patterns and cheating-like behaviour. Sophisticated software is used to compare candidates' answers from across the country. This data forensic work can reveal information that is shared with the regulatory authority of the province/territory in which you write. At that time, an investigation could be launched with or without your knowledge.

Consequences of Cheating

The consequences of cheating or behaviour that is viewed as suspicious can be serious and may include:

1. Being given a failing result on the exam. This counts towards the limited number of times (three) that you can write the exam;
2. Having a complaint filed against you;
3. Being denied entry into the practical nursing profession by the regulatory authority; and
4. Having a civil lawsuit filed against you.

Reporting Cheating

While you have a responsibility to be ethical, you also have an obligation to report unethical behaviour. In fact, some standards of practice and ethical codes require that professionals report unethical behaviour, which would include cheating or cheating schemes. In the exam process, this might include:

1. Reporting someone who has requested that you disclose the content of exam questions to them after you write the CPNRE.
2. Reporting someone who has written the CPNRE and is now offering to share confidential information on exam questions with you.

If you suspect cheating, please contact the Cheating Hotline by phone toll-free at 1-888-900-0005. You can also e-mail at cheating@asinc.ca.

Cheating includes sharing, copying, publishing or providing to anyone exam questions or answers by any means, including in person, telephone, electronically or digitally. Cheating also includes giving a summary or recollection of a question to someone else by any means.

All calls and e-mails will be handled discreetly and confidentially.

4

4

Taking the Practice Exam

Taking the Practice Exam

How you complete the Practice Exam will depend on whether you are using Method A, B or C (described in Chapter 1). If you are going to take the Practice Exam only once, gain the maximum benefit from this experience by attempting to simulate the actual exam conditions as closely as possible. That means writing the exam in a quiet location without the benefit of books, notes or other aids and strictly adhering to the time limit.

Since there are no experimental questions being tested on the Practice Exam (i.e., all the questions will count toward your total score), you should limit yourself to 3 hours and 45 minutes. Experimental questions are included in the Test Book of the actual CPNRE. Therefore, you will be allowed more time to complete the exam. During the CPNRE, you will have 4 hours.

Read the instructions contained in the Practice Exam carefully, but keep in mind that during your simulation, you will not have the benefit of a presiding officer to remind you of how much time is remaining. The front and back covers of the Practice Exam and the instructions are similar to those on the CPNRE. On the cover of the Practice Exam is a *test form number* that is also repeated in the lower left-hand corner of each page of the Test Book. This test form number is required by ASI for scoring the CPNRE (i.e., not the Practice Exam).

There are blank answer sheets included with the prep guide so that you can gain experience in recording the personal information and filling in the ovals that correspond to your answer selections. Familiarize yourself with the candidate information you will be required to complete when you write the CPNRE.

You should wait until you have finished the entire Practice Exam to calculate your total score and to create your Performance Profile. The information will be complete and, therefore, more accurate and more useful to you. Instructions on calculating your score and determining your Performance Profile are provided in Chapters 5 and 6 which follow the Practice Exam.

If you prefer taking the Practice Exam on the computer using the enclosed CD-ROM, your result and Performance Profile will be generated automatically once you have completed the exam in the *testing mode.*

TEST FORM 2701101 **SECRET**

The Canadian Practical Nurse Registration Examination

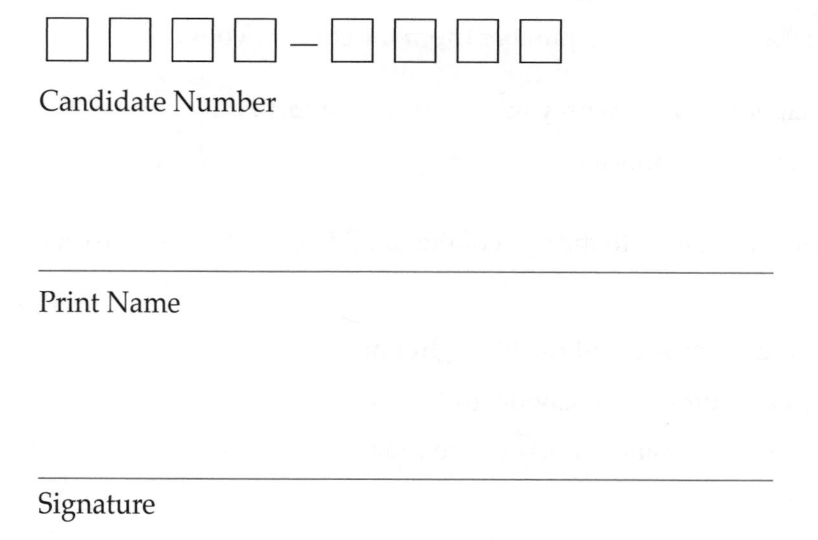

Candidate Number

Print Name

Signature

Read the instructions and sample questions inside the front cover

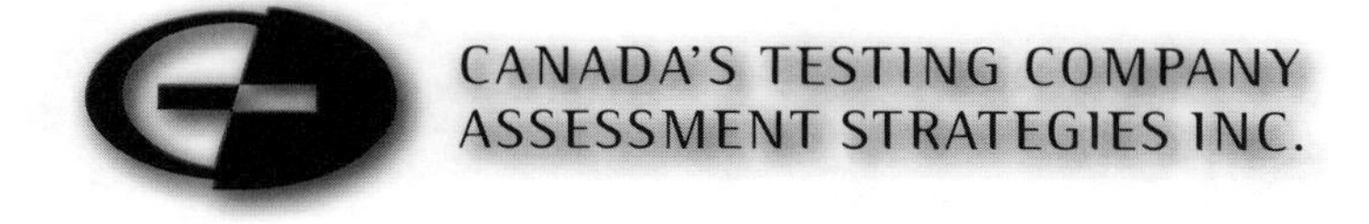

Instructions

(NOTE: THE FOLLOWING ARE INSTRUCTIONS THAT YOU WILL RECEIVE WHEN TAKING THE CPNRE.)

A) TESTING TIME AND MATERIAL

You will have 4 hours to complete the CPNRE. The starting and finishing times will be announced and you will be advised when there are 30 and 15 minutes working time remaining. If at any time you have any questions about what you should do, raise your hand and an invigilator will assist you.

Clear your desk of all materials except your identification card, answer sheet, test book, pencils and eraser. **Do not fold, bend or tear your answer sheet, as this could affect the scoring of your test.**

You will be advised whether you may leave the exam room if you finish the test before the time is up. You must stop working when the signal is given. An invigilator will check your test book and answer sheet before you leave.

B) ANSWER SHEET

Mark **ALL** of your answers directly on the answer sheet – **no credit** will be given for answers marked only in the test book.

Complete the identification portion of your answer sheet:

- Print your name, writing centre code, date of writing the exam and the name of the exam;
- Print and fill in the seven-digit form number (from the cover of your test book).

If you have a candidate label provided with your identification card:

- Detach the label from the identification card and place the label in the appropriate location on the answer sheet.
- **DO NOT** fill in the information to the right of the candidate label unless the candidate label is incorrect.

If you DO NOT have a candidate label, fill the top right portion of the answer sheet:

- Fill in the oval corresponding to the language of writing;
- Print your candidate number and writing centre code AND fill the corresponding oval for each digit.

Sign your name above the examination questions section.

Ensure to completely fill in the ovals. Do not fill in more than one oval for a question or you will not get credit for it. There may be fewer questions in the test book than provided on the answer sheet.

Verify that the question number from your test book corresponds to the number you have selected on your answer sheet.

Erase **completely** any answer you wish to change and mark your new choice in the correct oval. An incomplete erasure may be read incorrectly as an intended answer.

Do not press too heavily on your pencil or you may damage the answer sheet. Stray marks on the answer sheet may count against you.

You may use the margins of the test book for any scratch work, but you will not get credit for anything you write in the test book.

Once you've completed your exam, take 5 minutes and complete the candidate feedback survey. Use the survey section below the examination questions section.

C) TEST BOOK

Print AND sign your name on the lines on the cover of this test book and copy your candidate number into the appropriate boxes.

Read each question carefully and choose the answer that you think is the best. If you cannot decide on an answer to a question, go on to the next one and come back to this question later if you have time. Try to answer all questions. Marks are not subtracted for wrong answers. If you are not sure of an answer, it will be to your advantage to guess. It will probably be best to start at the beginning of the test book and work through the questions in order.

This exam contains a number of experimental questions being tested for future use. Your answers to these questions will not count toward your score. Because you will not be able to tell which questions are experimental, you should do your best on all questions, but do not spend too much time on any question.

The questions in the exam are presented as cases or as independent questions. The context of some cases may seem similar to others in your test book. This reflects current practice where a practical nurse may have to care for different persons with similar problems. Each case, however, tests different nursing content. The sample case on the next page shows the types of questions used. Correct answers are blackened in the ovals below the question.

Sample Case

Mr. Martin, 68 years old, is admitted to hospital with a diagnosis of pneumonia. The physician's orders include bedrest, oxygen therapy by mask and incentive spirometer every 1 to 2 hours.

The next FOUR (4) questions refer to this case.

1. Mr. Martin becomes upset when he learns he must stay in bed. Which approach should the practical nurse use when establishing a rapport with Mr. Martin?

1. "Hello, Mr. Martin. I will be caring for you today and I am here to see that you follow the physician's orders."
2. "Good morning, Mr. Martin. I hear you are unhappy about being put on bedrest."
3. "Good morning, Mr. Martin. I understand you are upset about being on bedrest, but it's only for a few days."
4. "Hello, Mr. Martin. I understand you have been put on bedrest. How do you feel about that?"

2. Mr. Martin is receiving oxygen as ordered. While changing his bed, the practical nurse notices that the television has a frayed wire. Which action should the practical nurse take immediately?

1. Turn off the oxygen and report the situation.
2. Turn off and unplug the television, attach a "do not use" sign and report the situation.
3. Make arrangements to have Mr. Martin's television exchanged for one in safe working order.
4. Caution Mr. Martin not to use the television until someone checks it.

3. The practical nurse has been asked to assist Mr. Martin with his breathing and coughing exercises. Which action should the practical nurse take to promote his performance?

1. Encourage Mr. Martin to inhale slowly and exhale rapidly.
2. Instruct Mr. Martin to use his spirometer every hour.
3. Ensure that Mr. Martin is in a supine position when performing his breathing exercises.
4. Explain to Mr. Martin that the best time to cough up secretions is in the evening before going to sleep.

1 ● 3 4

4. Which action should the practical nurse implement when providing mouth care for Mr. Martin?

1. Ensure that oral hygiene is completed every 2 to 3 hours.
2. Wear sterile gloves.
3. Provide mouthwash at the bedside.
4. Keep the humidifier bottle filled with normal saline.

● 2 3 4

End of Sample Case

Practice Exam
CASE

Mr. Robichaud is a 75-year-old married man who has mid-stage Alzheimer's disease. He was recently admitted to a long-term care facility.

The next FOUR (4) questions refer to this case.

---

1. What question should the practical nurse ask Mrs. Robichaud to obtain the most relevant information for updating the care plan?

1. "Do you have any help at home?"
2. "Are your children worried about their father?"
3. "What help does Mr. Robichaud require each day?"
4. "How frequently are you able to visit?"

---

2. Mr. Robichaud's son, Pierre, asks the practical nurse whether he can participate in his father's daily care when he is available. What should the practical nurse do?

1. Invite Pierre to come and play cards with his father.
2. Encourage Pierre to spend his days off with his father.
3. Reassure Pierre that his father's daily care is being provided by the health-care team.
4. Question Pierre about what part of his father's daily care he would like to be involved in.

4

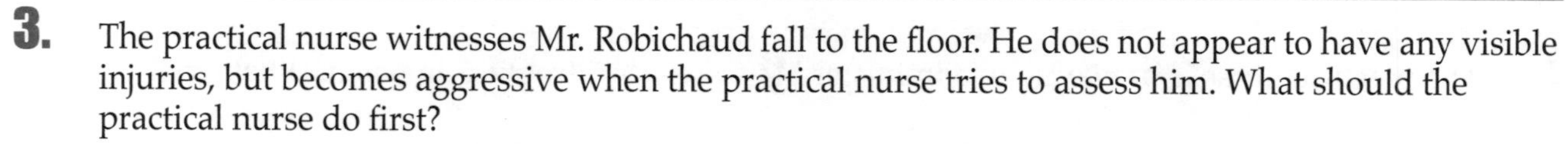

3. The practical nurse witnesses Mr. Robichaud fall to the floor. He does not appear to have any visible injuries, but becomes aggressive when the practical nurse tries to assess him. What should the practical nurse do first?

1. Reassure Mr. Robichaud and request assistance with a mechanical lift.
2. Stay with him and ask the nurse-in-charge to contact Mrs. Robichaud.
3. Wait until Mr. Robichaud becomes calm and complete the assessment of his injuries.
4. Call for assistance, reassure Mr. Robichaud and provide necessary care.

---

4. The practical nurse is helping orientate a new employee, Jeanne, an unregulated health worker. The practical nurse watches Jeanne helping Mr. Robichaud at mealtimes and notices that she appears uncomfortable. What should the practical nurse do?

1. Suggest that Jeanne share her concerns with the other employees.
2. Partner Jeanne with a more experienced unregulated health worker.
3. Invite Jeanne to attend information sessions on Alzheimer's disease.
4. Ask Jeanne how she feels about caring for clients with Alzheimer's disease.

End of Case

CASE

Mr. Cosmic, 68 years old, was transferred to the medical unit following a myocardial infarction (MI). His medical history includes type 2 diabetes mellitus. His orders include IV 0.9% NaCl at 30 mL/h, oxygen p.r.n., an oral hypoglycemic daily, nitroglycerin transdermal patch (Nitro-Dur) 0.4 mg daily and nitroglycerin 0.3 mg sublingual p.r.n for chest discomfort.

The next FIVE (5) questions refer to this case.

---

5. While washing Mr. Cosmic's back during morning care, the practical nurse notices a reddened area on his sacrum. What would demonstrate proper documentation of the practical nurse's assessment findings?

1. Small reddened area noted over sacrum
2. Reddened area noted over sacrum the size of a grape
3. Reddened area over sacrum 3 cm in diameter, skin intact
4. Skin over sacral area appears reddened

---

6. When giving Mr. Cosmic his oral hypoglycemic pill, he states "this does not look like the pill I take at home." What should the practical nurse do first?

1. Reassure Mr. Cosmic that this is the correct medication ordered by the physician.
2. Reassure Mr. Cosmic that this is the correct medication although it may look different.
3. Re-check the physician order and the home medication history.
4. Re-check the pharmacy label before giving the medication.

---

7. The practical nurse is preparing to administer Mr. Cosmic's nitroglycerin patch. What would be the best place to apply the patch?

1. Lower leg
2. Upper arm
3. Lumbar area
4. Upper thigh

---

8. The second day on the medical unit, Mr. Cosmic develops diarrhea and begins vomiting. The physician orders the IV rate increased to 150 mL/h. Two hours later, the practical nurse notices that he is dyspneic and his RR is 32 breaths/min. The practical nurse auscultates his chest and notes adventitious sounds throughout. What should the practical nurse do first?

1. Discontinue the IV infusion and notify the physician.
2. Reassess the IV rate and encourage deep breathing and coughing exercises.
3. Maintain the IV infusion at 150 mL/h and notify the physician.
4. Notify the physician and anticipate a decrease in the IV rate.

9. On the fourth day on the medical unit, Mr. Cosmic reports that he has chest discomfort and shortness of breath. The practical nurse notes that he is pale, and his skin is cool and clammy. What sequence of interventions is most appropriate?

1. Assess vital signs and blood glucose, and then apply oxygen.
2. Apply oxygen, assess vital signs and then assess blood glucose.
3. Assess vital signs, apply oxygen and then give sublingual nitroglycerin.
4. Apply oxygen, assess vital signs and provide a warm blanket.

End of Case

CASE

Jenny, 13 years old, has been hospitalized with vomiting and generalized stomach pain. Her parents are worried about her recent changing behaviour and depressed mood.

The next THREE (3) questions refer to this case.

10. Jenny tells the practical nurse that her stomach hurts because she is making herself vomit. Jenny asks the practical nurse not to tell. How should the practical nurse respond?

1. Tell Jenny that the practical nurse is only obligated to report vomiting if it occurs during her hospitalization.
2. Remind Jenny that clients have the right to determine what information is documented and reported.
3. Explain to Jenny that information is shared with the health-care team to provide appropriate care.
4. Reassure Jenny that her stomach pains will subside once she stops vomiting and her condition improves.

11. In accordance with the nursing care plan, the practical nurse sits with Jenny while she eats her meals and accompanies her to the bathroom. Today, the practical nurse notices Jenny's facecloths are missing from the bathroom. What action should the practical nurse take?

1. Discuss the issue of lost facecloths, search the room when Jenny is out of her room and document appropriately.
2. Ask Jenny where the facecloths are, ask her to return them and chart the missing facecloths.
3. Ask Jenny where the facecloths are and chart the suspicion that they are being used to hide uneaten food.
4. Discuss the issue of lost facecloths with Jenny and document appropriate information.

12. Jenny is very concerned about her weight. She exercises and makes food choices based on not wanting to become fat. She says that she does not feel like eating. What should the practical nurse do?

1. Design a diet in consultation with the dietitian and ensure that it is balanced, contains variety and has the requisite caloric intake.
2. Ask Jenny what she likes and dislikes, have her mother bring in food, and obtain and record her weight daily to demonstrate progress.
3. Include Jenny in goal-setting for healthy weight, have her maintain a food and fitness journal, and obtain and record her weight weekly.
4. Promote a healthy lifestyle, the importance of stress management and nutritional teaching with peer support groups.

End of Case

CASE

Mr. Smythe, a 75-year-old client with tuberculosis (TB), has been placed on isolation precautions since being admitted to the hospital.

The next THREE (3) questions refer to this case.

---

13. Which action best indicates that the practical nurse knows how to collect a sputum specimen from Mr. Smythe?

1. Keep the specimen at room temperature and send to the laboratory for analysis.
2. Collect the specimen in a clean, light occlusive container.
3. Instruct Mr. Smythe to use mouthwash prior to specimen collection.
4. Teach Mr. Smythe to deep breath and cough prior to expectoration.

---

14. While in Mr. Smythe's room doing routine care, what is the most crucial health information about TB that the practical nurse should provide to Mr. Smythe?

1. His contacts do not need to worry about contracting TB.
2. He must comply with medication protocol on discharge.
3. He should follow a well-balanced diet.
4. His fluid intake should ensure adequate hydration.

---

15. What would offer the best protection to the practical nurse when providing direct care to Mr. Smythe?

1. A mask
2. Sterile gloves
3. A gown
4. Goggles

End of Case

CASE

Mrs. Azzu, 68 years old, has chronic renal failure. She has been on peritoneal dialysis for the past 2 years. Her daughter brought her to the Emergency Department last night with a fever. Infection of her peritoneal dialysis catheter site is suspected.

The next FOUR (4) questions refer to this case.

---

16. Mrs. Azzu is started on IV therapy. What complication would be most likely to occur because of renal failure?

1. Infiltration
2. Fluid overload
3. Dehydration
4. Urinary retention

---

17. As Mrs. Azzu's hemoglobin is low, she is ordered ferrous sulfate (Slow-Fe). What side effect should the practical nurse tell Mrs. Azzu to expect?

1. Yellowing of the sclera
2. Rust-coloured urine
3. Discolouration of nail beds
4. Black-coloured stools

4

---

18. Mrs. Azzu reports swelling in her ankles. Yesterday, she had an intake of 1,000 mL and an output of 400 mL. When assessing Mrs. Azzu's respiratory status, what would the practical nurse most likely expect to find?

1. Inspiratory stridor bilaterally
2. Fine crackles in the bases bilaterally
3. Coarse crackles on auscultation
4. Vesicular breath sounds

---

19. The practical nurse checks Mrs. Azzu's blood test results. Her sodium and creatinine levels are elevated, and her potassium is 6 mmol/L. When health teaching, which food should the practical nurse encourage Mrs. Azzu to avoid consuming?

1. Orange juice
2. Green beans
3. Breads
4. Pineapple

End of Case

CASE

Mr. Lemay, 24 years old, was involved in a cycling collision. He is admitted to the unit following open reduction of a fractured left femur.

The next THREE (3) questions refer to this case.

---

20. Mr. Lemay is refusing to have his dressing changed. What should the practical nurse do first?

1. Ask Mr. Lemay if he needs an analgesic.
2. Ask Mr. Lemay what would be the best time to change his dressing.
3. Inform Mr. Lemay that the dressing must be changed now.
4. Explore the reasons for Mr. Lemay's refusal of treatment.

---

21. Approximately 1 hour after Mr. Lemay's return from the operating room, the practical nurse notices that Mr. Lemay's dressing has a large red stain. After assessing that the vital signs are normal, what should the practical nurse do next?

1. Elevate the left leg on two pillows.
2. Lower the head of the bed.
3. Cover the site with a pressure dressing.
4. Outline the stain and add the date and time.

---

22. Which observation would indicate to the practical nurse that Mr. Lemay has thoroughly understood teaching regarding the use of crutches?

1. The crutches are in contact with Mr. Lemay's axillae.
2. When climbing stairs, Mr. Lemay first places both crutches parallel on the first step.
3. To sit, Mr. Lemay first holds both crutches on the side opposite his injured leg.
4. Mr. Lemay wears soft, comfortable slippers.

End of Case

CASE

Emily, 10 months old, lives on a busy family farm where pesticides are used. Her father, who handles the pesticides, changed his clothes following a spray but left his boots by the back door. Later in the day, Emily is found playing near the back door. She quickly shows signs of illness and is rushed to the hospital.

The next FOUR (4) questions refer to this case.

---

23. The practical nurse is acting as a liaison between the interprofessional team and the family, and provides frequent updates on Emily's condition. What environment would be most appropriate for the practical nurse to use to communicate with Emily's family?

1. The hospital waiting room
2. A private room
3. The hospital chapel
4. In Emily's room

---

24. Emily goes into respiratory arrest and is resuscitated. The physician speaks with the family about Emily's progress but they find it difficult to understand the information. How could the practical nurse help the family understand the information the physician has provided?

1. Suggest that the family contact the Poison Control Centre.
2. Provide the family with poison control literature.
3. Encourage the family to ask questions and continue to clarify.
4. Have a social worker speak with the family.

4

---

25. Two weeks later, Emily is transferred to the pediatric unit. Her swallow reflex is diminished and enteral feeding with an indwelling nasogastric tube has been initiated. During the feeding process, the practical nurse has difficulty with the tube clogging. What should the practical nurse do?

1. Elevate the syringe to increase the flow rate.
2. Use the plunger of the syringe to apply more pressure.
3. Flush the tubing with tepid tap water.
4. Remove the tubing and reinsert new tubing.

---

26. After several months, the physician determines that Emily is palliative. The difficult decision to terminate life support is made. How can the practical nurse help support this family?

1. Encourage the family to withdraw from Emily's care.
2. Encourage the family to advocate for a private nurse.
3. Encourage a plan of care that involves the family's participation.
4. Encourage the family to make funeral arrangements in advance.

End of Case

CASE

Derek, 17 years old, is admitted to the surgical unit following a skiing accident. He has two fractured ribs, a fractured left wrist and a fractured left femur. He has a cast on his wrist.

The next THREE (3) questions refer to this case.

---

27. After the practical nurse assesses Derek's injuries, what will require immediate action?

1. Left fingers have some movement with a capillary refill of 4 seconds.
2. Left foot has a palpable pedal pulse and is slightly cooler than the right.
3. Left fingers are slightly swollen and bruised.
4. Left foot is warm with some pain on movement.

---

28. Why would the practical nurse consider Derek at risk for developing a fat embolism?

1. Wrist fracture
2. High-fat diet
3. Dehydration
4. Fractured femur

---

29. What should be included when teaching Derek about decreasing the risk of respiratory complications?

1. Splint chest with both hands when coughing.
2. Encourage the use of an incentive spirometer.
3. Alternate position frequently from side to side.
4. Use the overhead trapeze to facilitate mobility.

End of Case

CASE

Mr. Spencer, 52 years old with schizophrenia, lives in an apartment building. The practical nurse visits Mr. Spencer daily for medication administration and a mental status assessment. Lately, there have been reports from other tenants that Mr. Spencer hammers on the walls and yells for the noises to go away. Mr. Spencer risks being evicted if he does not stop. During today's visit, Mr. Spencer is pacing, stating that the noises in his head are loud, and he has his hands over his ears. He has not bathed lately and his apartment has garbage on the floor.

The next FOUR (4) questions refer to this case.

---

30. How should the practical nurse document the visit to Mr. Spencer's apartment?

1. Client pacing, states noises are loud, unkempt presentation, garbage all over floor. Landlord reports client is yelling and hammering on the walls and could get evicted if behaviour does not stop.
2. Client agitated and behaving inappropriately. Landlord reports client yelling and hammering on the wall and may get evicted. Client unkempt and apartment unclean.
3. Client pacing and is hallucinating. Landlord reports that client is yelling loudly, is hammering on the walls and he could get evicted if the behaviour does not stop. Apartment is a mess.
4. Landlord states tenants are complaining and client may be evicted due to inappropriate activity in client's apartment. Client is dirty and unkempt.

---

31. The practical nurse needs to advocate for the client. What is the best way to accomplish this?

1. Request that a social worker meet with Mr. Spencer about his situation.
2. Go to the landlord, apologize on behalf of the client and propose a new plan of care.
3. Ask the landlord to allow more time before evicting Mr. Spencer.
4. Inform Mr. Spencer that he must apologize to the landlord immediately.

---

32. While visiting Mr. Spencer, the practical nurse wants to discuss concerns with the client regarding his mental status and current living situation. Which is the best approach to use with Mr. Spencer?

1. Explain to Mr. Spencer that his behaviour is very inappropriate, it is going to get him evicted and he will end up homeless again.
2. Inform him that the voices need to be addressed by the psychiatrist and explain that the other tenants are frightened by the banging.
3. Tell Mr. Spencer that he could end up on the streets if he does not get his life organized.
4. Validate that the noises are bothersome and a visit to the psychiatrist may help. Explain that other tenants are troubled by the banging.

---

33. Which plan of care would be most appropriate for the practical nurse to implement for Mr. Spencer?

1. Notify the physician of Mr. Spencer's behavioural changes and request immediate hospitalization.
2. Suggest to Mr. Spencer that he move to an assisted-living facility before he gets evicted.
3. Advocate for a psychiatric assessment and increased daily visits by an appropriate health-care provider.
4. Advise Mr. Spencer that if he does not improve, he may be discharged from the program.

End of Case

CASE

Mrs. Proud, 32 years old, is pregnant for the third time. Her first pregnancy ended at 17 weeks' gestation and her second child was delivered at 36 weeks' gestation.

The next FOUR (4) questions refer to this case.

---

34. Mrs. Proud is full term and in early labour. How should the practical nurse record her obstetrical history?

1. Gravida 2, para 3
2. Gravida 2, para 2
3. Gravida 3, para 2
4. Gravida 3, para 1

---

35. Six hours later, Mrs. Proud's cervix is 100% effaced and 9 cm dilated. She is restless and crying out in discomfort. In which stage of labour is Mrs. Proud?

1. First stage of labour in the latent phase
2. Early in the third stage of labour
3. Early in the second stage of labour
4. First stage of labour in the transition phase

---

36. Mrs. Proud spontaneously delivers a living female. At 1 minute of age, the newborn is pink, has acrocyanosis, flexed tone, an apical pulse rate of 140 beats/min and responds with a vigorous cry to a tap on the sole of her foot. Which Apgar score would the baby receive?

1. 7
2. 8
3. 9
4. 10

---

37. Two hours after delivery, Mrs. Proud's fundus is firm, three fingerbreadths above the umbilicus, displaced to the right side, the size of a large grapefruit and slightly tender. She has a moderate amount of lochia rubra. What is the best action for the practical nurse to take?

1. Ask Mrs. Proud to void and re-assess the fundus.
2. Check when Mrs. Proud last received analgesic medication.
3. Notify the physician of the findings and monitor closely.
4. Massage the fundus until it returns to midline.

End of Case

CASE

Mr. Manne, 45 years old, is admitted with weight loss not yet diagnosed. He reports a loss of appetite and a general feeling of fatigue.

The next FOUR (4) questions refer to this case.

---

38. Mr. Manne is experiencing bloody diarrhea. What diagnostic tests would be ordered if colorectal cancer is suspected?

1. Upper GI series and electrolytes
2. Colposcopy and stool for occult blood
3. Colonoscopy and hemoglobin
4. Lower GI series and creatinine

---

39. Mr. Manne has surgery for colorectal cancer with the formation of a colostomy. While performing a dressing change, the practical nurse notices that Mr. Manne's stoma is swollen and bluish in colour. What should the practical nurse do first?

1. Continue with the dressing change.
2. Request that the surgeon be notified.
3. Leave a message with the physician's office.
4. Document these findings and report at change of shift.

---

40. Mr. Manne tells the practical nurse that his father died at the age of 50 from colon cancer. Mr. Manne states, "I am going to end up like my father." How should the practical nurse respond to Mr. Manne?

1. "You are not your father. You were diagnosed early."
2. "You think you are going to die, don't you?"
3. "You seem upset. Tell me what the physician has told you."
4. "Let's discuss getting you home. That will cheer you up, don't you think?"

---

41. While receiving discharge teaching, Mr. Manne asks the practical nurse what to expect in the descending colostomy pouch on a regular basis. What should the practical nurse respond?

1. Liquid stool
2. Semi-formed stool
3. Solid stool
4. No stool

End of Case

CASE

Mr. Rao, 45 years old, has been admitted following an open cholecystectomy. He has a nasogastric (NG) tube in place connected to suction and an IV.

The next FIVE (5) questions refer to this case.

---

42. In the past 2 hours, Mr. Rao's NG output totals 1,500 mL. After assessing his vital signs, what should the practical nurse do first?

1. Assess the client's pain.
2. Ask a colleague to assess the NG output.
3. Continue to monitor the NG output.
4. Ensure that the physician is notified.

---

43. The physician ordered 5,000 units of heparin sodium (Hepalean) subcutaneous twice a day. The vial of heparin sodium contains 10,000 units/1 mL. How much solution should the practical nurse withdraw?

1. 0.2 mL
2. 0.5 mL
3. 2 mL
4. 5 mL

---

44. Mr. Rao's dressing is saturated with serosanguineous drainage. How should the practical nurse cleanse the wound?

1. From distal to proximal
2. From proximal to distal
3. From medial to proximal
4. From proximal to medial

---

45. Mr. Rao pulls his IV out. What should the practical nurse do first?

1. Put on sterile gloves and elevate the extremity.
2. Put on clean gloves and apply pressure.
3. Apply pressure to the site and notify the nurse-in-charge.
4. Stop the IV and prepare for reinsertion.

---

46. On the third postoperative day, Mr. Rao's NG tube has been removed. His IV continues to infuse at 75 mL/h, and he is on clear fluids. Over the past 12 hours, his urinary output has been 220 mL. What should the practical nurse do first?

1. Palpate the bladder.
2. Ensure that the physician is notified.
3. Observe for signs of fluid balance.
4. Request an order for a diuretic.

End of Case

CASE

Mr. Goldwing, 68 years old, has Parkinson's disease. He has been admitted to an acute care unit, accompanied by his wife.

The next THREE (3) questions refer to this case.

47. Mr. Goldwing has been ordered an IV solution infusing at 125 mL/h. In a 24-hour period, how many mL would he receive?

1. 1,500 mL
2. 2,000 mL
3. 2,400 mL
4. 3,000 mL

48. Laboratory results indicate that Mr. Goldwing's hemoglobin is 80 g/dL. The physician orders 2 units of packed cells. What should the practical nurse do first?

1. Take his temperature, blood pressure, pulse and respiration rate.
2. Prime the blood administration set with D5W.
3. Have the physician contacted to verify the order.
4. Ensure that the emergency cart is in the room.

49. Mr. Goldwing has tremors and is unsteady while walking. What should the practical nurse do?

1. Hold the client's hand while walking down the hallways.
2. Give the client a walker when he is walking around the unit.
3. Ask the client if he needs any assistance for walking.
4. Ask the client's wife to assist him while walking.

End of Case

CASE

Joan is a 17-year-old, 155-cm-tall female, who normally weighs 48 kg. She has lost 9 kg in the past 3 months and has amenorrhea. Joan describes an intense fear of gaining weight and is preoccupied with food. She is admitted with a diagnosis of anorexia nervosa and is confined to the unit.

The next FOUR (4) questions refer to this case.

---

50. Joan's lunch consists of a small bowl of soup, a dinner roll, a spinach salad and a pot of tea. What should the practical nurse do to meet the responsibility of recording food intake?

1. Be present to remove her dinner tray and note what was eaten.
2. Ask Joan to record her intake and provide her with an intake/output sheet.
3. Remain with Joan while she eats and observe her intake.
4. Continue with normal duties and periodically return to check what Joan has eaten.

---

51. Which clinical manifestation is Joan likely to exhibit?

1. Fever
2. Dry skin
3. Coarse hair
4. Hypertension

---

52. After 8 weeks, Joan has gained 5 kg. She expresses concern about the weight gain and observes that her "thighs seem huge." Which response would be most therapeutic for the practical nurse to make?

1. "It must seem like that to you. Let's stand side-by-side and look in the mirror. You'll see your thighs aren't that big."
2. "It must be frightening for you to have gained so much weight. Let's talk about that with the psychologist."
3. "I hear your concerns. You are uncomfortable with how you see yourself and eating."
4. "You have gone through a great deal. Perhaps shopping for clothes that don't emphasize your weight gain would help you feel better."

---

53. At the third weekly interprofessional conference, Joan states that her preoccupation with food and exercise has greatly diminished. The practical nurse has observed Joan discussing recipes with other clients and lengthening her daily exercises. What should the practical nurse do?

1. Confirm for Joan and her family that she appears to be making progress and that her progress has been noted in her treatment plan.
2. Discuss the observations with Joan's family, noting specific changes in Joan's behaviour from the previous planning conference.
3. Encourage Joan to reflect on her behaviour and explore if she is less preoccupied with food and weight gain.
4. Introduce the need to begin discharge planning for Joan that includes referral to a local self-help group.

End of Case

CASE

Mrs. Hart is 39 years old, married with two children aged 10 and 13. She is admitted for a mastectomy following a diagnosis of right breast cancer. She is fearful the cancer has spread and is anxious about the future for herself and her family.

The next THREE (3) questions refer to this case.

---

54. Which action would best help Mrs. Hart reduce anxiety on the day she is admitted for her surgery?

1. Show her around the unit.
2. Offer her a backrub.
3. Listen to her concerns.
4. Encourage her to write in a journal.

---

55. Which action is most important for the practical nurse to perform on the morning of Mrs. Hart's first postoperative day?

1. Ask Mrs. Hart if she has been passing any flatus.
2. Encourage Mrs. Hart to do deep breathing and coughing exercises every 4 hours.
3. Assess Mrs. Hart's right mastectomy dressing for drainage.
4. Teach Mrs. Hart how to do wall-walking exercises.

---

56. On the second postoperative day, which action by the practical nurse would be most appropriate when assisting Mrs. Hart with morning care?

1. Encourage Mrs. Hart to brush her hair using her hand on her affected side.
2. Suggest to Mrs. Hart that she avoid looking at the incision until the drain is removed.
3. Recommend to Mrs. Hart that she wear a hospital gown so as not to soil her clothing.
4. Give Mrs. Hart perineal care to avoid strain on her affected arm and hand.

End of Case

CASE

Mrs. Mayhew, 72 years old, has been admitted to hospital with chronic obstructive pulmonary disease (COPD). She is accompanied by her daughter, Adrianna, who indicates that her mother's condition has deteriorated.

The next FIVE (5) questions refer to this case.

---

57. When taking Mrs. Mayhew's vital signs, the practical nurse assesses her respirations at 24 breaths/min. Which action should the practical nurse take first?

1. Obtain further information prior to reporting the findings.
2. Report the findings immediately to the nurse-in-charge.
3. Inform the physician during the next visit.
4. Document the respiration rate on the vital signs record.

---

58. Which action should the practical nurse take to promote Mrs. Mayhew's comfort?

1. Position in semi-Fowler's position.
2. Place both of her arms on pillows.
3. Assist her to a recliner and elevate her feet.
4. Encourage her to lean forward while sitting.

---

59. Mrs. Mayhew wears dentures. Which action is most important for the practical nurse to take when cleaning Mrs. Mayhew's dentures?

1. Brush the dentures in a circular motion.
2. Cleanse the dentures under hot running water.
3. Rinse the dentures with warm water.
4. Use a hard-bristled toothbrush.

---

60. Mrs. Mayhew goes for a walk down the hallway. What is correct documentation by the practical nurse?

1. Walking in hallway with no shortness of breath
2. Mrs. Mayhew up walking in hallway
3. Tolerating activities well
4. Activities of daily living completed this morning

---

61. Mrs. Mayhew is to be discharged today. Which activity should the practical nurse suggest to promote Mrs. Mayhew's independence?

1. Be as active as possible without increasing shortness of breath.
2. Walk to the corner store once a day.
3. Do all housework at one time so she can rest afterward.
4. Go to the mall to avoid social isolation.

End of Case

CASE

Mrs. Wong, 74 years old, has been admitted to a medical unit with a diagnosis of tuberculosis (TB). She has an order for oxygen 3 L/min via nasal cannula p.r.n. Mrs. Wong is in an isolation room and has airborne precautions in place. Because Mrs. Wong does not speak English, her daughter visits frequently.

The next FIVE (5) questions refer to this case.

---

62. The practical nurse sees Mrs. Wong's daughter in the hall. She approaches the daughter, who states that she finds it difficult to speak with her mother while wearing a mask. What is the most appropriate response for the practical nurse to make?

1. "Hospital policy states that all clients with TB must be placed in isolation."
2. "It's very important for you to wear the mask for your own protection."
3. "It will be okay. It is dangerous for you to be exposed to your mother's disease."
4. "It must be very frustrating. Try speaking loudly so she can hear you."

---

63. Mrs. Wong requires routine blood work but becomes upset and resists attempts to obtain her blood. Mrs. Wong needs further explanation about the procedure. Which intervention by the practical nurse would be the most appropriate?

1. Use non-verbal communication techniques such as hand gestures to explain the procedure.
2. Ask Mrs. Wong's daughter to facilitate communication with the practical nurse.
3. Explain to the physician that the client is resistant and the procedure cannot be completed.
4. Reschedule the blood work for when a hospital interpreter will be available.

4

---

64. The practical nurse notes that Mrs. Wong is dyspneic and slightly cyanotic. Her vital signs are T 39.2 °C, HR 112, RR 32 and BP 146/90. In what order should the practical nurse proceed?

1. Administer oxygen, contact Mrs. Wong's daughter, obtain an oxygen saturation level (SpO_2) and have the physician notified.
2. Have the physician notified, administer an antipyretic, perform a chest assessment and administer oxygen.
3. Obtain an oxygen saturation level (SpO_2), administer oxygen p.r.n., perform a chest assessment and have the physician notified.
4. Instruct her to perform deep breathing and coughing, administer oxygen, have the physician notified and contact Mrs. Wong's daughter.

65. Mrs. Wong's white blood cell (WBC) count is elevated. Considering Mrs. Wong's health status, what do these results indicate?

1. Dehydration due to hyperthermia
2. The presence of a high number of antibody titres
3. An inflammatory and possibly infectious process
4. Hypervolemia due to liver failure

66. Mrs. Wong is preparing for discharge. She asks whether she should continue taking her TB medications at home. What would be the best response by the practical nurse?

1. "Here are some written discharge instructions. If you have any questions, you can contact your physician."
2. "Contact your pharmacist who will provide instructions on how the medication should be taken."
3. "You must follow the treatment regimen by taking your medication and reporting for follow-up screening."
4. "The public health nurse will visit in a few days and discuss follow-up care with you."

End of Case

CASE

Ms. O'Connor, 67 years old, has been living alone in her family home. She has just been admitted by ambulance to an acute care facility. She has acute osteoarthritis and this has made self-care impossible. Upon admission, the physician has ordered Ms. O'Connor to be on complete bedrest for 48 hours.

The next FOUR (4) questions refer to this case.

---

67. The physician has ordered that splints be applied to Ms. O'Connor's hands and wrists at bedtime. What should the practical nurse do before applying these splints?

1. Ensure that Ms. O'Connor has a bedpan available.
2. Place Ms. O'Connor's hands in a hyperextended position.
3. Obtain Ms. O'Connor's permission to apply these splints.
4. Place Ms. O'Connor's hands in a flexed position.

---

68. Which action by the practical nurse would be most helpful in assisting Ms. O'Connor to use the bedpan?

1. Warm Ms. O'Connor's metal bedpan by rinsing it with warm water.
2. Turn Ms. O'Connor on her side and then roll her onto a fracture (slipper) bedpan.
3. Raise Ms. O'Connor to high-Fowler's position and have her lift her pelvis.
4. Leave Ms. O'Connor with the privacy drapes pulled and allow 15 minutes before returning.

---

69. Ms. O'Connor's condition has been slowly improving over the past 5 days and she is now allowed to ambulate with the use of a walker. What should the practical nurse do to promote Ms. O'Connor's safety when she is assisted from the bedside to the walker?

1. Assess Ms. O'Connor's motivation for ambulating with a walker.
2. Ensure that Ms. O'Connor is wearing well-fitting, non-skid shoes.
3. Instruct Ms. O'Connor to place her feet about 5 cm apart.
4. Encourage Ms. O'Connor to hold her back straight and to look ahead.

---

70. Ms. O'Connor's acute stage of arthritis has subsided. What should the practical nurse do first to promote Ms. O'Connor's independence?

1. Instruct her to sit up in the chair for her meals.
2. Allow her 20 minutes to complete morning care.
3. Encourage her to practise using her walker outdoors.
4. Talk with her about patterns of activity and rest.

End of Case

Independent Questions

QUESTIONS 71 to 180 do not refer to a case.

71. During admission, Mrs. Luniza, 72 years old, is confused about person, place and time. What should the practical nurse do first?

1. Assess mental health status.
2. Perform a Mini-Mental State Examination.
3. Assess for medication side effects.
4. Perform a neurological assessment.

72. Before changing an IV container, which action should be taken by the practical nurse first?

1. Review the client's intake/output for the shift.
2. Check the physician's order.
3. Gather the necessary equipment.
4. Explain the procedure to the client.

73. When using a mechanical lift to transfer Mr. Gosselin, 42 years old, from bed to chair, what should the practical nurse do first?

1. Place the bed in the lowest horizontal position.
2. Ensure that the brakes are locked on his bed.
3. Place Mr. Gosselin in high-Fowler's position.
4. Lower both side rails for good body mechanics.

74. The practical nurse is assessing the elimination of a client with suspected cystitis. What question should the practical nurse ask this client?

1. "Are you voiding large amounts of urine?"
2. "Is your urine dark brown in colour?"
3. "Does your urine have an odour similar to ammonia?"
4. "Do you feel that you are voiding more often?"

75. Mr. Hutmacher, 67 years old, received teaching regarding changing his colostomy appliance. How could the practical nurse best assess Mr. Hutmacher's learning?

1. Ask what problems he has had with the appliance.
2. Watch him change his appliance.
3. Check if the appliance is properly attached.
4. Look at his appliance site.

76. When providing mouth care for a client who wears dentures, what should the practical nurse do first?

1. Wear a mask to prevent spread of disease.
2. Offer the client a denture toothbrush, toothpaste and mouthwash.
3. Verify the physician's orders.
4. Apply gloves prior to removing dentures.

77. Mrs. Caron, 92 years old, is confused and disoriented. The interprofessional team decides that she may ambulate on the unit only if she is supervised. A few days later, Mrs. Caron is lucid and insists that she be allowed to ambulate alone. What should the practical nurse do?

1. Continue to supervise Mrs. Caron until the interprofessional team is consulted.
2. Ask Mrs. Caron if a family member would be available to walk with her.
3. Encourage Mrs. Caron to continue complying with the safety measure.
4. Respect Mrs. Caron's wishes and allow her to ambulate alone.

78. A 2-year-old client has an IV infusing through an infusion control device. Which action by the practical nurse is most appropriate when the device is being used?

1. Monitor the infusion control device every 15 minutes.
2. Attach a mini-drop administration set to the infusion control device.
3. Check that the infusion control device rate is set properly.
4. Monitor the infusion control device every 2 hours.

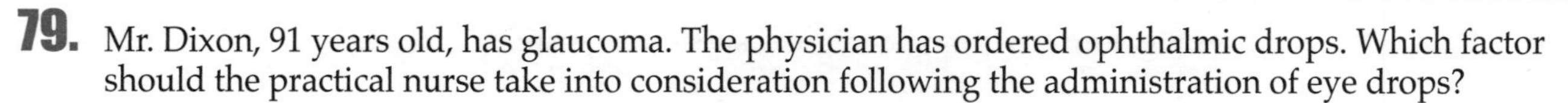

79. Mr. Dixon, 91 years old, has glaucoma. The physician has ordered ophthalmic drops. Which factor should the practical nurse take into consideration following the administration of eye drops?

1. Instruct Mr. Dixon to squeeze his eyelids shut.
2. Press on the nasolacrimal duct for several seconds.
3. Gently wipe excess fluid from outer to inner canthus.
4. Teach Mr. Dixon to hyperextend his head for 5 minutes.

80. Jared, 4 years old, is diagnosed with acute bronchial asthma. Jared's mother states, "The physician told me that my smoking makes his asthma worse. Is this true? I want to quit, but I just don't know how to." What is the best response for the practical nurse to make?

1. "You should discuss this with your physician who can recommend the best plan for you to stop smoking."
2. "You will need to stop smoking for the welfare of your child. Would you like to contact the lung association?"
3. "Cigarette smoke can cause an asthmatic episode. If you would like to quit, I can help you create a plan."
4. "It is dangerous for children with asthma to be exposed to cigarette smoke. You need to quit right away."

81. Mr. Rogers, 22 years old, weighs 90 kg and is 165 cm tall. He is to receive IM iron dextran (Dexiron) daily. Which site would be most appropriate for administering this medication?

1. Deltoid
2. Vastus lateralis
3. Ventrogluteal
4. Dorsogluteal

---

82. Mrs. Sopczak, 65 years old, had back surgery. What would the practical nurse use to logroll her in bed?

1. Trapeze
2. Turning sheet
3. Trochanter roll
4. Sliding board

---

83. Mrs. Peterson, 72 years old, is receiving a blood transfusion. Two hours later, the practical nurse notices that the client has become dyspneic and her heart rate has increased from 76 to 104 beats/min. What should the practical nurse do first?

1. Auscultate the client's chest.
2. Stop the transfusion.
3. Verify the client's O_2 saturation levels.
4. Take the client's temperature.

---

84. What is the maximum volume that can be injected subcutaneously?

1. 0.5 mL
2. 1 mL
3. 2 mL
4. 3 mL

---

85. Mr. Gerald, 82 years old, is a resident of a long-term care facility. He has become quiet and sits alone in his room all day. Which nursing intervention would best assist the practical nurse in identifying the reason for his social isolation?

1. Establish whether hearing and vision deficits exist.
2. Ask his family to describe his typical behaviour.
3. Arrange for a psychiatric assessment.
4. Check his blood work for an electrolyte imbalance.

86. During an IV assessment, the practical nurse finds an empty secondary medication bag hanging with a label for dimenhydrinate (Gravol). The client is wearing an arm band that indicates that he has an allergy to dimenhydrinate. What should the practical nurse do first?

1. Document in the clinical record.
2. Assess for nausea and vomiting.
3. Have the physician contacted.
4. Complete an incident report.

87. What should the practical nurse do when changing a simple sterile dressing?

1. Wear sterile gloves to remove the dressing.
2. Obtain a specimen from the wound for culture and sensitivity.
3. Cleanse the surrounding skin area prior to cleansing the incision line.
4. Dispose of the dressing in a bag/container.

88. Ms. May, 78 years old, is admitted to the palliative care unit. What information would help the practical nurse best determine Ms. May's spiritual needs?

1. Her sources of strength and meaning of life
2. Her level of knowledge regarding her prognosis
3. Her pre-planned funeral preferences
4. Her resuscitation status and advance directives

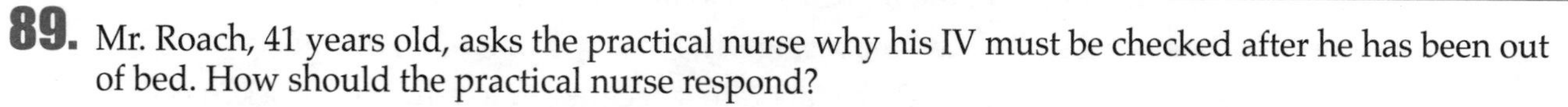

89. Mr. Roach, 41 years old, asks the practical nurse why his IV must be checked after he has been out of bed. How should the practical nurse respond?

1. Moving can affect reaction to the IV infusion.
2. Moving may change the rate of flow.
3. Moving is likely to dislodge the IV needle.
4. Moving can disturb the regulation clamp.

90. When should the practical nurse have a replacement IV bag ready to hang?

1. At least 1 hour before needed
2. When the IV bag is empty
3. When the drip chamber is half full
4. As the solution empties into the drip chamber

91. A practical nurse has been given a client assignment that she believes is beyond her abilities. What should the practical nurse do first?

1. Request a change in assignment.
2. Provide care to the clients.
3. Ask a colleague to assist with client care.
4. Discuss feelings with her supervisor.

92. Mrs. Hochban, 62 years old, restricts her fluids because of urinary incontinence. What should the practical nurse do initially to assist Mrs. Hochban to regain control of her bladder?

1. Ask her to record her 24-hour urine output.
2. Instruct her in pelvic floor exercises.
3. Encourage her to drink cranberry juice.
4. Ensure that she voids every 1 to 2 hours.

93. Mrs. Block, 75 years old, has been admitted with congestive heart failure and is receiving an IV infusion of D5W at 125 mL/h. When the practical nurse is performing routine morning care, Mrs. Block reports a pounding headache, chills and difficulty breathing. Her pulse and BP are elevated. What should the practical nurse do initially?

1. Have the physician informed of her symptoms.
2. Help her to a sitting position on the side of the bed.
3. Decrease the IV rate of flow.
4. Obtain an oxygen saturation reading.

94. Ms. Findlay, 24 years old, is to receive 1 unit of whole blood. When taking the blood to Ms. Findlay's room, the practical nurse is asked by a staff member to also take a unit of packed cells to another client in the next room. What should the practical nurse do to promote safety in the identification of both clients?

1. Clarify the name and room of the second client with the staff member.
2. Take both units of blood and the requisitions to the two clients at the same time.
3. Return for the packed cells after delivering Ms. Findlay's unit of whole blood.
4. Request that the staff member ask the laboratory technician to return the packed cells.

95. The practical nurse is employed in a private residence caring for Ms. Jones, a 60-year-old woman with type 1 diabetes mellitus. One morning, Ms. Jones is found unconscious. What should the practical nurse do initially?

1. Check blood glucose.
2. Administer insulin.
3. Assess vital signs.
4. Ensure a patent airway.

96. The practical nurse arrives to help out on a busy surgical unit. The clerk informs the practical nurse that one client has been ringing for a bedpan for 10 minutes, another client has been calling out for pain medication for 5 minutes, and another client has just arrived from the operating room. Also, a visitor is at the desk demanding to speak to someone about her mother. In what order should the practical nurse proceed?

1. Speak to the visitor and then assess the client from the operating room.
2. Assess the client from the operating room and get the client medication for pain.
3. Give the client the bedpan and the other client medication for pain.
4. Get the client medication for pain and then assess the client from the operating room.

97. The practical nurse observes that a client with chronic obstructive pulmonary disease (COPD), Mr. Sanjeev, 74 years old, is dyspneic, restless and reporting chest discomfort. Expiratory wheezes are audible and he is diaphoretic. The bedding is saturated from urinary incontinence. What should the practical nurse do first?

1. Auscultate his chest.
2. Change his bed linens.
3. Apply oxygen at 1-2 L/min.
4. Assess vital signs.

---

98. Mrs. Bates, 68 years old, has rheumatoid arthritis and is being admitted to a nursing home. She has recently been diagnosed with early stage Alzheimer's disease. Her son manages her finances and her daughter has been responsible for personal care. From whom should the practical nurse obtain consent?

1. Son
2. Daughter
3. Client
4. Son and daughter

---

99. Mr. Ross, 75 years old, is having a bowel resection. What preoperative teaching should the practical nurse emphasize initially?

1. Modification of diet
2. Care of an ostomy
3. Deep breathing exercises
4. Postoperative positioning

---

100. Mrs. Gore will be given a mydriatic medication during her eye examination. What would the practical nurse do for Mrs. Gore prior to her leaving the clinic?

1. Instruct Mrs. Gore to wear sunglasses while driving.
2. Irrigate Mrs. Gore's eyes with sterile water.
3. Have Mrs. Gore wait in a darkened room for 15 minutes.
4. Inquire about Mrs. Gore's transportation from the clinic.

---

101. One of the practical nurse's co-workers complains that another colleague is lazy. How should the practical nurse initially respond?

1. Report these concerns to the nurse-in-charge for follow-up.
2. Ask if the co-worker has discussed this with the colleague.
3. Remind the co-worker of the colleague's heavy workload.
4. Offer to discuss these concerns with the colleague promptly.

102. What should the practical nurse do to help prevent external rotation of a client's lower limb?

1. Place a sheepskin on the client's bed.
2. Use an alternating pressure mattress.
3. Place a footboard at the client's feet.
4. Use a trochanter roll to maintain position.

---

103. Mr. Olsen, 75 years old, lives in a nursing home. He is diagnosed with mild dementia. Occasionally he attempts to get out of bed at night and is at risk for falls. What nursing intervention should the practical nurse use to ensure his safety?

1. Apply a p.r.n. restraint at night.
2. Restrict Mr. Olsen's fluid intake after 18:00.
3. Place the bed in the lowest position at bedtime.
4. Ensure that the side rails are up at bedtime.

---

104. Mr. Frost, 24 years old, has a diagnosis of quadriplegia and lives in an assisted-living facility. Following a night of beer drinking, he states that he is hungry, has a throbbing headache and feels sweaty. His orders include acetaminophen (Tylenol) 650 mg orally every 6 hours p.r.n. How should the practical nurse proceed?

1. Verify his blood sugar levels.
2. Assess his vital signs.
3. Administer the prescribed analgesic.
4. Position him flat in bed.

---

105. Mrs. Bourgoin, 72 years old, is receiving IV therapy of 0.9% NaCl 1,000 mL with 40 mEq of KCl (potassium chloride) infusing at 100 mL/h. Her oral furosemide (Lasix) was discontinued when her IV therapy was initiated. What piece of information about the client is most significant?

1. She is no longer short of breath.
2. She has increased urinary output.
3. She eats a banana every morning.
4. She has elevated serum potassium levels.

---

106. Mr. Sutton had a colostomy 8 days ago and is ready for discharge. He is comfortable with his colostomy but feels anxious about life outside the hospital. What could the practical nurse do to best support Mr. Sutton?

1. Reassure him that all will go well if he manages his care as instructed.
2. Encourage him to return to the unit if he has any further questions.
3. Provide him with pamphlets outlining colostomy care.
4. Offer him contact information for local support groups.

107. Mrs. North, 65 years old, has a deep vein thrombosis and is receiving an anticoagulant. Which instruction would be most important for the practical nurse to include when teaching Mrs. North about her medication?

1. Elevate the legs with pillows under the knees when resting supine.
2. Use an electric razor if shaving underarms and legs.
3. Apply firm pressure to cuts for approximately 30 seconds to stop bleeding.
4. Exercise the affected leg if pain and swelling return.

108. The practical nurse enters a client's room at 08:00 and notices pills in a medication cup on the nightstand. The pills are a p.r.n. analgesic that were signed out at 07:30. The agency policy states that pills are not late if given within 30 minutes of the time ordered. What should the practical nurse do?

1. Let the client take the pills if she is awake and wants to take them.
2. Complete an incident/occurrence report including the name of the colleague responsible.
3. Consult the nursing supervisor for further direction on how to proceed.
4. Remove the medications from the room and fill out an incident/occurrence report.

109. The practical nurse is directed to monitor a client's intake and output in order to calculate fluid balance. Which item should be included in intake?

1. Urinary catheter irrigation
2. Blood transfusions
3. Bowl of watermelon
4. Nasogastric drainage

110. Ms. Huard, 59 years old, is scheduled for a permanent colostomy. Which strategy is most important in preoperative health teaching?

1. Anticipate that Ms. Huard will have a body image disturbance.
2. Identify Ms. Huard's current knowledge level of colostomy care.
3. Provide Ms. Huard with pictures that clearly explain the types of colostomies.
4. Arrange for Ms. Huard to meet with the colostomy support group.

111. Mrs. Cormier, 67 years old, had a bowel resection and now has a colostomy. When preparing Mrs. Cormier for discharge, what should the practical nurse do first?

1. Inform Mrs. Cormier that an enterostomal therapist will demonstrate colostomy care.
2. Provide brochures on where Mrs. Cormier can purchase colostomy supplies.
3. Give Mrs. Cormier a demonstration on how to change the colostomy bag.
4. Ask Mrs. Cormier to describe her concerns regarding colostomy care at home.

112. Mrs. Morrow, 69 years old, has expressive aphasia and requires a dressing change to her right hand. Which action by Mrs. Morrow would best imply consent to the procedure?

1. Getting out of bed into the chair
2. Holding out her right hand
3. Turning onto her right side
4. Sitting up at the bedside

---

113. Which conditions would lead the practical nurse to place a client on droplet precautions?

1. Measles, chickenpox and varicella
2. Influenza, rubella and mumps
3. Clostridium difficile, Escherichia coli and hepatitis A
4. Impetigo, scabies and herpes simplex

---

114. Mrs. Akbar, 65 years old, had a hip replacement yesterday. She has been unable to void for 10 hours. How should the practical nurse proceed?

1. Perform a straight catheterization.
2. Offer Mrs. Akbar the use of a fracture bedpan.
3. Encourage Mrs. Akbar to drink additional fluids.
4. Check the physician's orders on the chart.

---

115. The practical nurse administers a medication via an incorrect route. What must the practical nurse do immediately following discovery of the error?

1. Assess and report the effectiveness of the administered medication.
2. Inform the appropriate person and the client of the error immediately.
3. Record the administration of the medication on the client's chart.
4. Assess the client's condition and report the medication error.

---

116. Which action by the practical nurse represents appropriate application of a restraint?

1. Apply a jacket restraint under the client's clothing.
2. Tie the straps of an ankle restraint to the side rails.
3. Remove wrist restraints at least twice a day.
4. Tie the straps of an ankle restraint with a quick-release knot.

---

117. When preparing to change the IV solution bag, which action should the practical nurse consider to promote client safety?

1. Compare solution to the previous IV bag.
2. Check the physician's order.
3. Change the IV tubing set.
4. Wear gloves during the procedure.

118. Mr. Cooper, 76 years old, returned from the operating room 2 hours ago and is reluctant to deep breathe. What should the practical nurse do initially?

1. Reinforce the importance of deep breathing.
2. Determine the need for pain medication.
3. Assess his reluctance to deep breathe.
4. Assist him to a more comfortable position.

---

119. Mrs. Simpson places her inhaler in a drawer immediately after use. Which instruction should the practical nurse give to Mrs. Simpson?

1. Clean the inhaler with rubbing alcohol and water.
2. Rinse the inhaler with warm water.
3. Soak the inhaler in hydrogen peroxide and water.
4. Wipe the inhaler with a cloth.

---

120. Ms. Fleisher, a 72-year-old nursing home resident, tells the practical nurse, "I'm no good anymore. Don't waste your time caring for me." How should the practical nurse respond?

1. Tell Ms. Fleisher that she has a lot of good qualities.
2. Discuss with Ms. Fleisher ways to address these feelings.
3. Suggest that Ms. Fleisher find a friend within the facility.
4. Reassure Ms. Fleisher that she has never been a bother.

---

121. What should the practical nurse do when shaving a client with a safety razor?

1. Soak the face with a warm washcloth prior to shaving.
2. Hold the skin loosely over the area to be shaven.
3. Shave the area by using long, firm strokes.
4. Use strokes in the opposite direction of hair growth.

---

122. While assessing Brian, 3 years old, for the first time in the clinic, the practical nurse observes numerous fresh and faded bruises. His chart has numerous references to injuries. The mother states that he is one of four active boys who play roughly. What are the practical nurse's responsibilities?

1. Ensure that these observations are reported.
2. Refer to the local police department.
3. Discuss age-appropriate activities with Brian's mother.
4. Speak with Brian privately and ask him about the bruises.

123. Mr. Pieris, 42 years old, has been diagnosed with angina. What approach should the practical nurse take first to encourage a healthy lifestyle and minimize progression of the disease?

1. Provide Mr. Pieris with pamphlets about his condition.
2. Ask about risk factors related to cardiovascular disease.
3. Refer Mr. Pieris to a cardiac support group.
4. Discuss lifestyle changes and develop a teaching plan.

---

124. What is the rationale for positioning a client in a left lateral position for an enema?

1. To decrease vagal nerve stimulation
2. To promote effective sphincter control
3. To make it easier for the client to expel the fluid
4. To allow gravity to take the fluid into the colon

---

125. A practical nurse hears a colleague speaking to a client in a rude and inappropriate manner in the client's room. What action should the practical nurse take?

1. Knock on the door and observe the situation.
2. Check on the client and complete an incident report.
3. Ask the colleague to apologize to the client.
4. Defuse the situation and talk to the colleague privately.

---

126. Mrs. Malloy, 69 years old, is crying in her hospital room. She explains to the practical nurse that her son has moved into her home against her wishes. What should the practical nurse do?

1. Refer the son to an outside housing agency.
2. Inform the son that his mother is upset.
3. Explore with the client the need to call the police.
4. Facilitate a referral within the health-care agency.

---

127. Mr. Chan, 72 years old, is in the terminal stage of cancer. His wife tells the practical nurse that Mr. Chan does not enjoy his meals anymore. Which response by the practical nurse is most appropriate?

1. Explore her concerns in further detail.
2. Inform her that Mr. Chan still needs nutrition.
3. Encourage her to make him eat something.
4. Ask her what she has done to help him eat.

---

128. Which meal provides the most balanced diet?

1. Baked potato, steak, carrots, coffee
2. Fish burger on a brown bun, milk, pear
3. Fried chicken, rice, apple pie, tea with milk
4. Vegetarian pizza, diet cola, strawberry Jell-O

129. What action by the practical nurse promotes increased fluid intake for a client with pneumonia?

1. Monitor intake throughout the shift.
2. Offer fluids that the client likes.
3. Keep ice chips at the bedside.
4. Record a list of favourite beverages.

130. The practical nurse notices a colleague reviewing the medical record of a friend who is not a client assigned to the colleague. What should the practical nurse do first?

1. Ask if the colleague has questions regarding the client's condition.
2. Notify the supervisor of the colleague's behaviour.
3. Encourage the colleague to speak to the friend about her condition.
4. Remind the colleague that client records are private.

131. A client reports excessive drowsiness after his scheduled narcotic administration. He says that he is pain free. What should the practical nurse do initially?

1. Have the physician notified and request a review of the medication.
2. Educate the client on the physical dangers of regular narcotic use.
3. Ask the client why he has not reported the effects of his medications sooner.
4. Monitor for further signs and symptoms of an allergic response.

4

132. Mrs. Abdul has multiple sclerosis. Some days, she has difficulty feeding herself but insists on doing so. How can the practical nurse best support Mrs. Abdul?

1. Be available for assistance when requested.
2. Inform her of the practical nurse's responsibility to feed her.
3. Cut up the difficult-to-chew foods into smaller pieces.
4. Provide Mrs. Abdul with a puréed diet.

133. Mrs. Wentzell, 2 days post-hysterectomy, becomes diaphoretic and apprehensive. She is assessed and found to be hypertensive, tachycardic and dyspneic with scant hemoptysis. What should the practical nurse do first?

1. Place in high-Fowler's position, have physician notified and request an analgesic.
2. Elevate the head of the bed, call for help and continue to monitor vital signs.
3. Turn the client on her left side and notify the nurse-in-charge.
4. Request anti-anxiety medication and remain with the client until anxiety decreases.

134. Mr. Keough, 42 years old, was admitted to the surgical unit postoperatively. The first of 2 units of packed cells is infusing at 100 mL/h. Mr. Keough informs the practical nurse of discomfort in his back, nausea and chills. What should the practical nurse do?

1. Administer pain medication and antiemetic and cover him with a warm blanket.
2. Inform him that the discomfort is related to his surgery and offer an analgesic.
3. Assess vital signs, inform the nurse-in-charge and document.
4. Stop the blood infusion, assess vital signs and have the physician notified.

---

135. Mr. Matthews requires medicated eye drops, one drop per eye every 2 hours for conjunctivitis. The practical nurse observes that Mr. Matthews' right eye is sealed closed with yellow secretions. What should the practical nurse do before instilling the drops?

1. Cleanse the right eye from inner to outer canthus with gauze moistened in normal saline and administer the medication into the lower conjunctival sac of each eye.
2. Administer the medication into the left eye only, apply a normal saline compress, and record and report the discharge.
3. Gently spread the eyelids with a gloved hand, cleanse the lower conjunctival sac with normal saline and administer the medication into the inner canthus of each eye.
4. Cleanse each eye with separate pieces of gauze moistened in normal saline and administer the medication into the outer canthus of each eye.

---

136. Mr. Scott, 28 years old, is discharged with a prescription for warfarin sodium (Coumadin) 2 mg daily. What does the practical nurse need to educate Mr. Scott about?

1. Avoid eating pork or pork by-products.
2. Expect to have frequent nose bleeds.
3. Limit his intake of green leafy vegetables.
4. Decrease activity to reduce chance of injury.

---

137. What should the practical nurse do initially when a client with a urinary catheter reports lower abdominal and perineal discomfort?

1. Report to the nurse-in-charge immediately.
2. Check for patency of the drainage system.
3. Reposition the client and irrigate the catheter.
4. Obtain a urine specimen for analysis.

---

138. What should the practical nurse do when providing care to a client with a colostomy?

1. Change the pouch on each shift.
2. Empty the pouch when it is full.
3. Irrigate the colostomy on each shift.
4. Empty the pouch when it is one-third full.

139. Mr. Ganga, 70 years old, is bedridden and has an order for a Foley catheter insertion. What would the practical nurse do first?

1. Position the client.
2. Wash hands.
3. Obtain consent.
4. Gather supplies.

140. Mrs. MacAulay, 84 years old, has an IV infusing at 125 mL/h. She is reporting shortness of breath. The practical nurse auscultates crackles in the base of her lungs. After having the physician notified, what should the practical nurse anticipate doing next?

1. Reducing the IV rate
2. Encouraging deep breathing and coughing
3. Monitoring urinary output
4. Assessing the apical heart rate

141. Mr. Stanley, 83 years old, has just been admitted to a nursing home. He shouts, "Let me out of here! I want to go home!" Which response by the practical nurse best demonstrates respect for Mr. Stanley?

1. "I'm sorry, but you can't go home Mr. Stanley."
2. "It must be hard for you to leave your home."
3. "Do not be upset Mr. Stanley. We will take good care of you."
4. "Would you like me to call your family?"

142. What should the practical nurse do immediately prior to obtaining blood or blood products from the blood bank?

1. Gather baseline vitals from the client.
2. Check for previous transfusion reactions.
3. Check the client's hemoglobin level.
4. Verify the physician's order.

143. Mr. Franklin's IV is leaking at the insertion site and needs to be changed. What is the first step in discontinuing his IV?

1. Support the cannula while removing the tape.
2. Put on sterile gloves.
3. Stop the flow by clamping off tubing.
4. Verify physician's order.

144. Mr. Barr, 67 years old and recently retired, has just been told by his physician that he has inoperable liver cancer. His wife is with him and it is obvious that they are both very upset. Which intervention by the practical nurse would best provide support to Mr. and Mrs. Barr?

1. Inform them that the hospital gives excellent care and has many skilled physicians.
2. Recognize the difficulty of the situation and ask if they would like some time alone.
3. Acknowledge their feelings, especially since they planned to travel upon retirement.
4. Encourage them to discuss their feelings and plan their remaining time together.

---

145. The practical nurse observed a colleague make an inappropriate hand gesture toward another colleague. What should the practical nurse do?

1. Report the incident to a supervisor immediately.
2. Advise the offender that this type of behaviour is inappropriate.
3. Ask the offender to provide a rationale for this gesture.
4. Suggest the offender apologize to the colleague immediately.

---

146. Mr. Wall, 72 years old, is preparing for discharge. He lives alone but his daughter lives in the same city. After discharge, he will require assistance with daily activities. Which action would be most appropriate to include in his discharge plan?

1. Recommend that he stay with his daughter for a few weeks.
2. Suggest that a neighbour check on him daily.
3. Recommend that a health-care worker provide assistance at home.
4. Suggest that he stay in hospital for a few more days.

---

147. Which manifestation indicates that a client is experiencing a complication as a result of IV infusion therapy?

1. Decreased blood pressure
2. Decreased skin turgor at the site
3. Increased skin temperature at the site
4. Increased perspiration

---

148. Mr. Desroches, 79 years old, has type 2 diabetes mellitus and is admitted to a care facility accompanied by his son. What should the practical nurse do to determine Mr. Desroches' care needs?

1. Identify ways to maintain a normal blood glucose level.
2. Consult Mr. Desroches about his care.
3. Ask the dietitian to identify a menu for Mr. Desroches.
4. Consult Mr. Desroches' son to identify the care for his father.

149. A client is scheduled for major surgery. The physician has ordered the client to be grouped and crossmatched for 2 units of whole blood. Which reason best explains the need for this order?

1. To replace blood volume loss
2. To maintain fluid volume
3. To increase the number of red blood cells
4. To provide plasma clotting factors

150. Sara, 18 years old, is admitted to the unit. After a course of IV therapy, the physician orders a clear fluid diet for Sara. Which fluid would be most appropriate for the practical nurse to offer Sara initially?

1. Milkshake
2. Flat ginger ale
3. Half-strength orange juice
4. Cream soup

151. While receiving IV infusion therapy, a client begins to experience symptoms of pulmonary edema. What action should the practical nurse take initially?

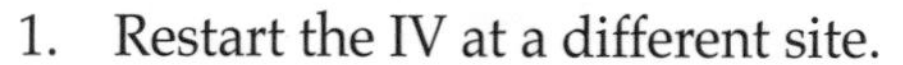

1. Restart the IV at a different site.
2. Discontinue the IV.
3. Increase the IV rate.
4. Decrease the IV rate.

152. A client with a diagnosis of type 1 diabetes mellitus has an IV infusion to keep the vein open. The practical nurse performs an initial assessment and observes that the solution of D5W is infusing at 50 mL/h. Which action by the practical nurse is most appropriate?

1. Decrease the rate of the infusion.
2. No action is required at this time.
3. Verify the physician's order.
4. Inform the nurse-in-charge of the rate of flow.

153. Mr. Shaw, 42 years old, underwent an incisional hernia repair yesterday. He informs the practical nurse that he has been doing his deep breathing exercises as instructed. What should the practical nurse do initially in response to Mr. Shaw's statement?

1. Observe Mr. Shaw as he does the breathing exercises.
2. Document the information as stated by Mr. Shaw.
3. Ask Mr. Shaw to explain the procedure for doing the deep breathing.
4. Encourage Mr. Shaw to add coughing to his exercises.

154. Mr. Schneider is a 75-year-old long-term care resident who has type 1 diabetes mellitus. Which observation should the practical nurse report immediately after providing nail care?

1. Calluses over the hand surface
2. Thickened fingernails
3. Hangnails on several fingers
4. Brittle, dry fingernails

155. A client who is on a restricted calorie diet requests a liquid nutritional supplement because he feels symptoms of a cold. Which response by the practical nurse would be most appropriate?

1. Provide the liquid nutritional supplement as requested.
2. Reinforce that he should follow Canada's Food Guide.
3. Suggest eating fresh citrus fruits to increase his energy levels.
4. Explain that liquid nutritional supplements are not included in his diet.

156. Mr. Marchbank, a 76-year-old client on the palliative care unit, has died. His wife requests that staff dress him in a suit. She states that, because of cultural beliefs, this time in hospital will be the only opportunity for the family to view the body. How should the practical nurse respond to this situation?

1. Explain that policy requires clients to remain in a hospital gown.
2. Ask the family to bring in the suit to the hospital.
3. Request that the hospital clergy speak with the family about their beliefs.
4. Suggest that the family dress the client in his suit.

157. Which statement by the practical nurse would provide the most empathetic response to a 92-year-old client's request to see his mother?

1. "It must be difficult for you to be alone."
2. "I am so sorry that your mother is away."
3. "I can try to locate your mother."
4. "Perhaps there is someone else I can contact."

158. A practical nurse and colleague are assisting Mrs. Bell, an 82-year-old paraplegic client, to bed. This facility requires the use of a mechanical lift for non-weight bearing clients but the colleague insists that the mechanical lift is unnecessary. What should the practical nurse do?

1. Perform the client transfer alone using the mechanical lift.
2. Work with the colleague to transfer the client to the bed without the lift.
3. Explain to the colleague that the client has functional limitations.
4. Remind the colleague that the policy should be followed.

159. Ms. Oskawski, 34 years old, has had diarrhea and vomiting for 3 days. What skin manifestation should the practical nurse anticipate?

1. Itchy skin
2. Reddened skin
3. Poor skin turgor
4. Mottled skin

160. Ms. Daly, 25 years old, has an order for insertion of a Foley catheter. What should the practical nurse do first?

1. Verify the order with a colleague.
2. Review the policy and procedure.
3. Explain the procedure to the client.
4. Obtain consent from the client.

161. Mr. Black, 45 years old, committed suicide while being treated for depression in hospital. What procedure is essential as a result of his death?

1. Family should be approached about organ donation.
2. Family must give consent prior to the autopsy.
3. The coroner must be notified.
4. Hospital liability must be investigated.

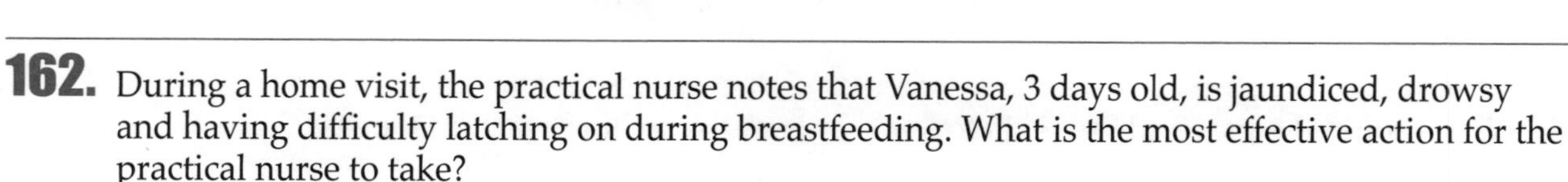

162. During a home visit, the practical nurse notes that Vanessa, 3 days old, is jaundiced, drowsy and having difficulty latching on during breastfeeding. What is the most effective action for the practical nurse to take?

1. Reassure the mother that jaundice is common and assist the baby to latch on.
2. Inform a lactation consultant and request assistance.
3. Advise Vanessa's mother to change to formula feeding.
4. Report the observations immediately because phototherapy may be required.

163. Mrs. Raabis, 65 years old, returned 2 hours ago from the recovery room following a bowel resection. The abdominal dressing has visible drainage, skin colour is dusky, incisional pain is rated at 8 on a scale of 0 to 10 and the IV site is leaking. What should the practical nurse do first?

1. Assess the IV site.
2. Administer oxygen.
3. Administer pain medication.
4. Mark drainage on the dressing.

164. Mr. Azizi, 90 years old, is in the hospital. His son feels that his father is no longer able to make decisions. The son indicates that he will be making decisions on his father's behalf. How should the practical nurse respond?

1. Comply with the son's request and document in the client's chart.
2. Notify the physician so that new consents for care can be signed.
3. Explain the process of becoming a substitute decision-maker to the son.
4. Organize a family conference to notify everyone of the change.

---

165. A client has an IV infusion with a microdrip ordered to infuse at 50 mL/h. The practical nurse checks the flow rate and counts 60 drops/min. Which action by the practical nurse is appropriate?

1. Decrease the flow to 20 drops/min.
2. Reduce the flow to 50 drops/min.
3. Increase the flow to 80 drops/min.
4. No action is required; the rate is as ordered.

---

166. The practical nurse is preparing to teach Mr. Hall, 30 years old, how to self-administer insulin. What best demonstrates that the client is ready to learn?

1. He desires to have his wife present during the entire teaching.
2. He asks to look at the syringe and needle.
3. He requests information on other medications for diabetes.
4. He becomes quiet when the practical nurse begins the demonstration.

---

167. What should the practical nurse do to teach a client to care for an artificial eye?

1. Wash the artificial eye in warm normal saline.
2. Clean the eye socket with a cotton ball moistened with an antiseptic solution.
3. Wipe from outer to inner canthus to remove crusts and secretions.
4. Store the artificial eye in a container filled with an antiseptic solution.

---

168. The practical nurse observes a co-worker putting two tablets of acetaminophen-caffeine-codeine phosphate (Tylenol No. 3) into her uniform pocket. When questioned, the co-worker states that the medication is intended for Mr. Arnold. However, Mr. Arnold was discharged 2 hours ago. What should the practical nurse do first?

1. Recommend that the co-worker return the medication immediately.
2. Report the incident to a supervisor immediately.
3. Document the occurrence on an incident form.
4. Verify the narcotics record to see if there are other discrepancies.

169. What factor would maintain the rate of flow of an IV infusion?

1. Tubing of the administration set is patent.
2. Level of solution in the container is low.
3. Height of the container is at eye level.
4. Drip chamber is three-quarters full.

170. Mr. Melanson, 45 years old, is receiving an IV of D5W at an ordered rate of 120 mL/h. Upon assessment, the flow rate is 12 drops/min. What should the practical nurse do when assessing the infusion?

1. Palpate Mr. Melanson's insertion site for heat indicating an infiltration.
2. Palpate the insertion site for coolness indicating an inflammation.
3. Inspect Mr. Melanson's IV tubing for patency to ensure there is no blockage.
4. Inspect the IV drip chamber for fluid volume to ensure that it is full.

171. The practical nurse is caring for Mr. Albert, 72 years old, who has peripheral vascular disease. When assisting him back to bed following ambulation, the practical nurse observes cool, edematous extremities due to venous stasis. What should the practical nurse do?

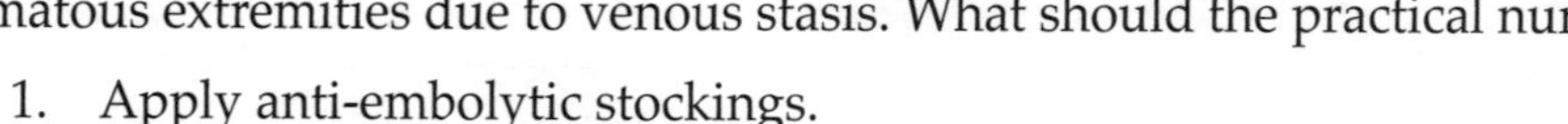

1. Apply anti-embolytic stockings.
2. Massage his legs and feet.
3. Wrap his legs in a warm blanket.
4. Elevate his legs above the level of the heart.

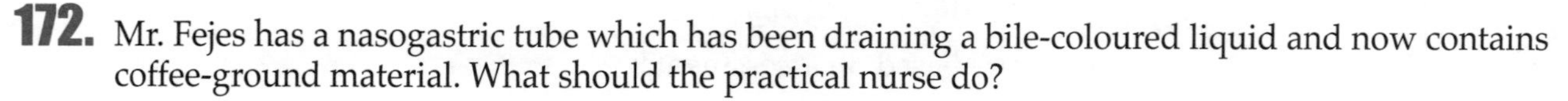

172. Mr. Fejes has a nasogastric tube which has been draining a bile-coloured liquid and now contains coffee-ground material. What should the practical nurse do?

1. Continue to observe the drainage.
2. Check the suction tubing for patency.
3. Report the findings to the physician.
4. Increase the power on the suction.

173. Mrs. Summer is a 70-year-old senior living in her own home. She requires weekly home-care visits to assist her with maintenance of her hypertension. Since she has no available family, Mrs. Summer asks the practical nurse to take her out for the evening. What should the practical nurse do?

1. Take Mrs. Summer out for the evening.
2. Take Mrs. Summer out if her next of kin is notified.
3. Tell Mrs. Summer that she will spend the evening with her at her home.
4. Suggest that a social worker visit Mrs. Summer to discuss her needs.

174. The practical nurse is assigned four clients: Ms. Law, who is 1 day postoperative and requesting assistance to the bathroom; Mr. Steel, who is 2 days postoperative and has a scheduled dressing change; Ms. Baran, who is 1 day postoperative and requests pain medication; and Mr. Logan, who is 2 days postoperative and requests something to drink. What client should the practical nurse see first?

1. Ms. Baran
2. Mr. Logan
3. Mr. Steel
4. Ms. Law

---

175. Mr. Baker, 50 years old, has developed a pressure ulcer on his left ankle. Which action by the practical nurse best demonstrates principles of medical asepsis when changing the dressing on the ulcer?

1. Wearing sterile gloves when changing the dressing
2. Wearing a mask and sterile gloves when changing the dressing
3. Washing hands prior to commencing the dressing change
4. Cleansing the ulcerated skin with hydrogen peroxide

---

176. Mrs. Rinka, 68 years old, has chronic renal failure, diabetes mellitus and peripheral neuropathy. She requires blood glucose monitoring every 2 hours and wound care on her left great toe. She receives peritoneal dialysis twice daily. Which action by the practical nurse indicates good time management?

1. Performing bedbath before doing blood glucose test
2. Consulting regularly with the team leader
3. Adjusting activities of care based on assessments
4. Organizing Mrs. Rinka's care around her dressing changes

---

177. Mrs. Morris is a client on the palliative care unit. Her husband states, "The physician has given me a lot of information about my wife, but I still have many questions." How should the practical nurse respond?

1. Review the information he has and offer to answer his questions.
2. Suggest that he write down his questions and offer to place them in his wife's chart.
3. Instruct him to talk with the nurse-in-charge to arrange a meeting with the physician.
4. Arrange for him to meet with the palliative care nurse specialist.

178. Ms. Lee, 73 years old, is admitted to a long-term care facility. Which action by the practical nurse would best fulfill Ms. Lee's need for psychological safety?

1. Place her on constant observation for 24 hours.
2. Provide her with a tour of the facility.
3. Give her a room with a pleasant view.
4. Ensure that her room has non-slip rugs.

179. Peter, 18 years old, has type 1 diabetes mellitus. The practical nurse reviews the diabetic education material with Peter. Which statement best indicates that Peter understands his condition?

1. "I have joined the gym, lowered my glucose intake and reduced the amount of insulin I take."
2. "I attend diabetic education classes, exercise daily and have stopped eating desserts."
3. "I monitor my glucose levels, alternate sites for my insulin and regulate my caloric intake."
4. "I regularly monitor my glucose levels and take insulin when I experience hyperglycemia."

180. Ashley, 16 years old, has been admitted to the ambulatory care unit for transfusion of 2 units of packed red blood cells. Ashley develops chills, dyspnea and tachycardia 15 minutes after initiation of the transfusion. What is the correct sequence of nursing actions?

1. Stop the transfusion, keep the vein open with normal saline, obtain client's vital signs and have the physician notified.
2. Run the normal saline, stop the blood transfusion, have the physician notified and monitor client's vital signs.
3. Check client's vital signs, stop the transfusion, keep the vein open with normal saline and have the physician notified.
4. Have the physician notified, stop the blood transfusion, keep the vein open with normal saline and monitor vital signs.

End of Independent Questions

End of Practice Exam

5

Scoring the Practice Exam

5

Scoring the Practice Exam

Calculating your score

The following steps can be used to calculate your total raw score for the Practice Exam.

Locate the answer key for the Practice Exam (found later in this chapter).

Tally up your responses that correspond to the correct answers indicated on the answer key. Identify those questions you answered incorrectly by circling or highlighting them on your answer sheet or by listing them on a separate sheet of paper. This will make it easier for you to create your Performance Profile, an exercise which is explained in the next chapter.

Score one point for each correct answer. There is no penalty for incorrect or blank responses; they receive a score of zero. Be sure to check your answer sheet for "double responses" to questions (i.e., where you selected more than one answer to a single question). Double responses are scored as zero, even if one of the answers selected is correct.

Use the chart below to record your total raw score.

Number of questions answered correctly

Total raw score .... ______/180

The next calculation you can make is to convert your total raw score into a percentage score. This may be done using the following formula:

Percentage Score

$$\frac{\text{Total raw score}}{180} \times 100 = \underline{\qquad}\%$$

Interpreting your score

Although the total raw score and percentage score that you calculate are of a different type than the result you would receive on the actual CPNRE (see next section), they can provide useful feedback on your performance. By using the score interpretation scale, you can obtain a quick assessment of your performance on the Practice Exam, along with some follow-up steps you should take to enhance your preparation for the CPNRE. Note that no specific pass mark is set for the Practice Exam.

How the CPNRE is scored

The CPNRE is computer scored by ASI. Only answers recorded on your answer sheet are scanned and scored. You will not receive any credit for questions that you only answered directly in the Test Book and not on the answer sheet. Likewise, credit will not be given where you selected more than one answer to a single question. It is essential that you read and follow the instructions inside the Test Book on how to correctly mark your selected answers; otherwise, your score may be adversely affected.

Once your answer sheet is scanned, your score on the exam is calculated and your "pass" or "fail" result is determined by comparing this score to the established standard (or pass mark).

The standard to be met on the CPNRE is established, prior to the administration of the exam, using a criterion-referenced approach. Such an approach involves setting the standard in reference to the content and the difficulty of the test questions. This is in contrast to a norm-referenced approach which sets the standard in relation to the performance of the candidates who write the exam.

The standard-setting procedure used involves convening panels of subject matter experts from across Canada to determine a point on a measurement scale that represents the expected performance of a minimally competent entry-level practical nurse. These subject matter experts are individuals who work closely with entry-level practical nurses and include educators, practitioners and administrators. Prior to performing their task, the subject matter experts are provided with an extensive orientation and training by ASI staff to ensure that they produce ratings based on the same understanding of the minimally competent entry-level practical nurse.

In addition to the expert ratings, a variety of relevant data are carefully considered to ensure that the standard that candidates will be required to achieve on the exam is valid and fair. This can include information on the preparation of new graduates, data on the performance of candidates on previously administered exams and pertinent psychometric research findings. Based on all of this information, a pass mark is set that represents the minimum acceptable standard.

Regardless of the version of the exam that is administered, a candidate's score is converted to a common measurement scale and compared against the established passing point on that scale. Although different forms of the exam contain different sets of questions, this conversion ensures that all candidates are treated fairly and are evaluated against the same standard. If your score on this common scale is at or higher than the passing point, you will receive a "pass" result on the exam and if your score is lower than the passing point, you will receive a "fail" result on the exam.

Your pass/fail result on the CPNRE is reported on an *Examination Report/Bulletin* that is sent to you by your regulatory authority. Candidates who fail the CPNRE are also provided with feedback on their test performance. This feedback is similar to the information you will obtain by creating your Performance Profile (see Chapter 6).

Score Interpretation Scale

Percentage Score	Performance Interpretation	Suggestions for Follow-Up

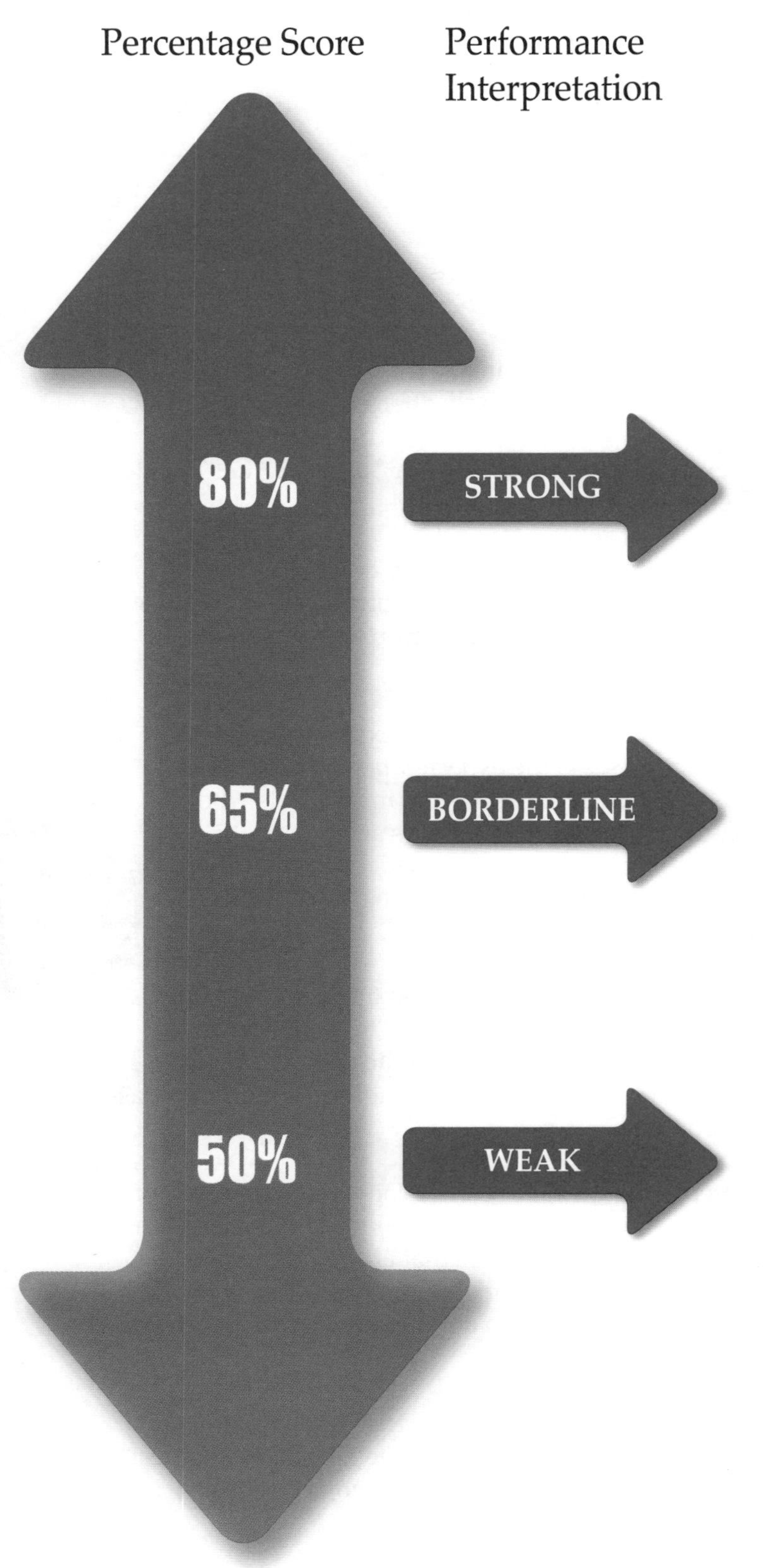

STRONG - Review the rationales of the questions you answered incorrectly. The closer your score is to the borderline zone, the more you should consult the relevant texts that are cited. As well, by creating your Performance Profile (see Chapter 6), you may identify specific areas on which you should focus during your remaining preparation time. Before writing the CPNRE, take another look at the Practice Exam questions that you answered incorrectly.

BORDERLINE - Create your Performance Profile to determine your areas of strength and weakness and follow the strategies provided for dealing with your weaknesses (see Chapter 6). Review some general practical nursing textbooks, concentrating on the problem areas and also consult textbooks specific to the problem areas. After your review, retake the Practice Exam before writing the actual CPNRE.

WEAK - Create your Performance Profile (see Chapter 6) to gain a better understanding of your areas of weakness in the competency categories. In addition to reviewing some key practical nursing textbooks, be sure to read the rationales for all the questions in the Practice Exam. You may also benefit from reviewing the test-taking strategies in Chapter 3. Finally, retake the Practice Exam before writing the actual CPNRE.

Answer key for prep guide Practice Exam

1. Answer: 3	37. Answer: 1	73. Answer: 2	109. Answer: 2	145. Answer: 2
2. Answer: 4	38. Answer: 3	74. Answer: 4	110. Answer: 2	146. Answer: 3
3. Answer: 4	39. Answer: 2	75. Answer: 2	111. Answer: 4	147. Answer: 3
4. Answer: 4	40. Answer: 3	76. Answer: 4	112. Answer: 2	148. Answer: 2
5. Answer: 3	41. Answer: 3	77. Answer: 4	113. Answer: 2	149. Answer: 1
6. Answer: 3	42. Answer: 4	78. Answer: 3	114. Answer: 2	150. Answer: 2
7. Answer: 2	43. Answer: 2	79. Answer: 2	115. Answer: 4	151. Answer: 4
8. Answer: 4	44. Answer: 2	80. Answer: 3	116. Answer: 4	152. Answer: 3
9. Answer: 3	45. Answer: 2	81. Answer: 3	117. Answer: 2	153. Answer: 1
10. Answer: 3	46. Answer: 3	82. Answer: 2	118. Answer: 3	154. Answer: 3
11. Answer: 4	47. Answer: 4	83. Answer: 2	119. Answer: 2	155. Answer: 4
12. Answer: 3	48. Answer: 1	84. Answer: 2	120. Answer: 2	156. Answer: 2
13. Answer: 4	49. Answer: 3	85. Answer: 1	121. Answer: 1	157. Answer: 1
14. Answer: 2	50. Answer: 3	86. Answer: 3	122. Answer: 1	158. Answer: 4
15. Answer: 1	51. Answer: 2	87. Answer: 4	123. Answer: 2	159. Answer: 3
16. Answer: 2	52. Answer: 3	88. Answer: 1	124. Answer: 4	160. Answer: 3
17. Answer: 4	53. Answer: 3	89. Answer: 2	125. Answer: 4	161. Answer: 3
18. Answer: 3	54. Answer: 3	90. Answer: 1	126. Answer: 4	162. Answer: 4
19. Answer: 1	55. Answer: 3	91. Answer: 4	127. Answer: 1	163. Answer: 2
20. Answer: 4	56. Answer: 1	92. Answer: 4	128. Answer: 2	164. Answer: 3
21. Answer: 4	57. Answer: 1	93. Answer: 3	129. Answer: 2	165. Answer: 2
22. Answer: 3	58. Answer: 4	94. Answer: 3	130. Answer: 4	166. Answer: 2
23. Answer: 2	59. Answer: 3	95. Answer: 4	131. Answer: 1	167. Answer: 1
24. Answer: 3	60. Answer: 1	96. Answer: 2	132. Answer: 1	168. Answer: 2
25. Answer: 3	61. Answer: 1	97. Answer: 3	133. Answer: 2	169. Answer: 1
26. Answer: 3	62. Answer: 2	98. Answer: 3	134. Answer: 4	170. Answer: 3
27. Answer: 1	63. Answer: 4	99. Answer: 3	135. Answer: 1	171. Answer: 4
28. Answer: 4	64. Answer: 3	100. Answer: 4	136. Answer: 3	172. Answer: 3
29. Answer: 2	65. Answer: 3	101. Answer: 2	137. Answer: 2	173. Answer: 4
30. Answer: 1	66. Answer: 3	102. Answer: 4	138. Answer: 4	174. Answer: 1
31. Answer: 1	67. Answer: 3	103. Answer: 3	139. Answer: 3	175. Answer: 3
32. Answer: 4	68. Answer: 2	104. Answer: 2	140. Answer: 1	176. Answer: 3
33. Answer: 3	69. Answer: 2	105. Answer: 4	141. Answer: 2	177. Answer: 1
34. Answer: 4	70. Answer: 4	106. Answer: 4	142. Answer: 4	178. Answer: 2
35. Answer: 4	71. Answer: 4	107. Answer: 2	143. Answer: 3	179. Answer: 3
36. Answer: 3	72. Answer: 2	108. Answer: 4	144. Answer: 2	180. Answer: 1

6

Creating Your Performance Profile

6

Creating Your Performance Profile

Once you have completed and scored the Practice Exam, it is possible to create a personalized Performance Profile that allows you to identify your areas of strength and weakness on the exam based on the competency categories and the cognitive levels. You will need your scored answer sheet (or a list of the questions you answered incorrectly), the Performance Profile Tally Sheet and the Performance Profile Chart (found in the Additional Materials section at the end of the prep guide) and a calculator.

Classification of Questions

Each question in the Practice Exam has been classified within two different classification schemes: Competency Category and Cognitive Level. Each question's classifications are indicated beside the question's rationales in Chapter 7.

These classification schemes are weighted elements from the *CPNRE Blueprint*. For a detailed explanation of the classifications, see Chapter 2.

Steps for Creating Your Performance Profile

Step 1 In chapter 5, you scored the Practice Exam and identified the questions you answered incorrectly. For each question answered incorrectly, place an X beside the corresponding classifications in the rationale section (see Chapter 7).

Step 2 The Performance Profile Tally Sheet and the Performance Profile Chart are located in the Additional Materials section at the back of the prep guide and can be easily removed. The Performance Profile Tally Sheet contains two tables. In Table 1 of the Tally Sheet, for each question you answered incorrectly, place a mark in the row that corresponds to the Competency Category for that question (see Sample — Step 2). Similarly, in Table 2, place a mark in the row that corresponds to the Cognitive Level for each question you answered incorrectly.

Sample Step 2 Performance Profile Tally Sheet

Table 1: Competency Category

Competency Categories		Total Incorrect		Total in Category	% Incorrect	
Professional, ethical and legal practice	~~||||~~		÷	37 ×	100 =	%
Foundations of practice	~~||||~~ ~~||||~~ |		÷	113 ×	100 =	%
Collaborative practice	~~||||~~ ~~||||~~ |||		÷	30 ×	100 =	%
Total Incorrect			÷	**180 ×**	**100 =**	%

Step 3 Total the marks in the rows to determine the number of questions you answered incorrectly in each category.

Step 4 Calculate the percentage of questions you answered incorrectly for each category. To calculate the percentage, divide the number of questions you answered incorrectly by the total number of questions for that category (found at the end of the row) and multiply by 100 (see Sample — Steps 3 and 4).

Sample Steps 3 and 4 Performance Profile Tally Sheet

Table 1: Competency Category

Competency Categories		Total Incorrect		Total in Category	% Incorrect		
Professional, ethical and legal practice	~~||||~~	5	÷	37 ×	100 =	14	%
Foundations of practice	~~||||~~ ~~||||~~ |	11	÷	113 ×	100 =	10	%
Collaborative practice	~~||||~~ ~~||||~~ |||	13	÷	30 ×	100 =	43	%
Total Incorrect		29	÷	**180 ×**	**100 =**	16	%

6

Step 5 Create your Performance Profile by taking the percentage values from each category and darkening the corresponding rows on the Performance Profile Chart (see Sample – Step 5).

Sample Step 5 Performance Profile Chart

Table 1: Competency Category

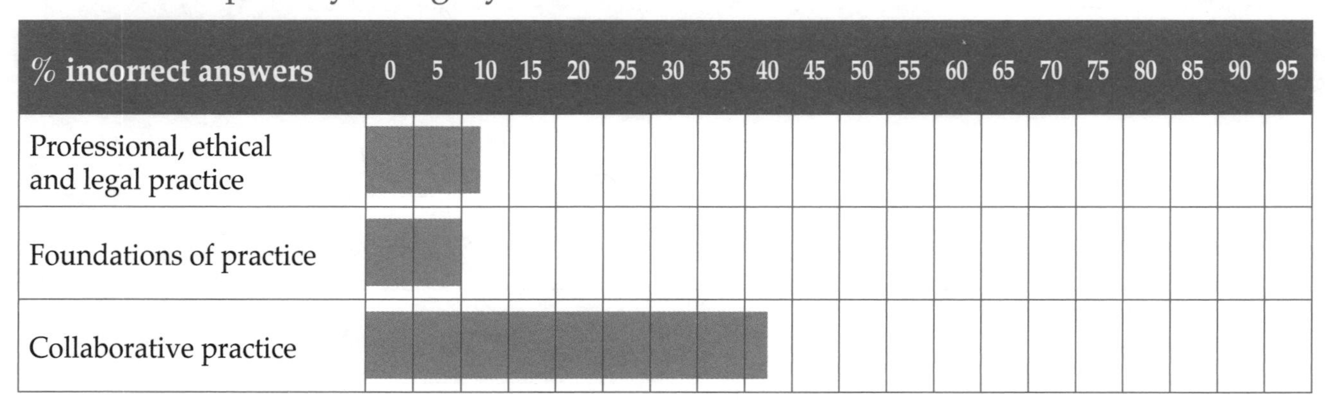

Interpretating Your Performance

The goal in creating your Performance Profile is to identify your areas of relative strength and weakness. This information can help you make the best use of your remaining preparation time.

Competency Category Results

Generally, those categories in which you selected a high percentage of incorrect answers are the areas you should focus on during your remaining preparation time. However, this approach can be further refined to arrive at a more accurate diagnosis.

In looking at each table on the Tally Sheets, you will notice that the number of questions in each category (i.e., the number by which you must divide) varies; some areas have relatively few questions whereas others have many. This is an important aspect in understanding your performance. Both the *percentage* of incorrect responses in a category and the total *number* of incorrect responses in a category should be carefully considered to make a complete interpretation of your performance.

You will recall that the Competency Category is a weighted element of the exam Blueprint. This means that the number of questions on the exam from each competency category is set and that this number is not equal for each category. The distribution of questions on the Practice Exam, by category, is as follows.

- **Professional, ethical and legal practice:** 21%
- **Foundations of practice:** 62%
- **Collaborative practice:** 17%

The following example will help to illustrate the importance of considering both the percentage and the number of incorrect responses in a category. If your Performance Profile Chart shows that you selected the highest percentage of incorrect answers in the Collaborative Practice category in Table 1, you should keep in mind that a relatively small number of questions on the CPNRE deals with Collaborative Practice (30 questions out of the total of 180). Even if you selected only correct responses for that category, the impact on your total score would be relatively small. On the other hand, a fairly small percentage of incorrect responses in the Foundations of Practice category (with 113 questions out of a total of 180) represents a relatively large number of questions on the exam. Consequently, improving your performance in this category by only a few percentage points can make a greater difference to your overall result.

Therefore, although a high percentage of incorrect responses in a competency category is certainly an indication of a weakness in that category, your best strategy for studying may require you to focus on another category, one that has a greater representation on the exam.

Once you have determined which competency categories you need to improve in, you may wish to follow the three steps below.

1. Go to Appendix A and review the competencies in the categories identified as areas of weakness for you; this will give you an overview of the competencies that require your attention.
2. Review the questions that are classified in the competency categories you have identified as weaker for you. Include in your review both the questions you answered correctly as well as those you answered incorrectly; this will give a more complete review of the content that measures the competencies you need to improve on. Be sure to read the rationales for the correct and incorrect responses to get a better understanding of your areas of weakness.
3. Look up the references cited (or other comparable references) for the questions you answered incorrectly; this can increase your understanding of material you may not have yet fully mastered.

Cognitive Level Category Results

The interpretation approach given for the competency categories also applies to your results in the Cognitive Level categories because it also represents a weighted element of the Blueprint.

- **Knowledge/Comprehension:** 11%
- **Application:** 51%
- **Critical Thinking:** 38%

As a strategy for dealing with your identified areas of weakness, you may wish to follow the three steps below.

1. Verify your understanding of the categories that are causing difficulties for you. This can be done by reviewing the definitions of these various categories (see Chapter 2). You should also note the relative weight of each category.
2. Review all the questions that have been classified within your weaker categories. Include the questions you answered correctly as well as those you answered incorrectly. This will provide you with a more complete review of the levels in question.
3. Look up the references cited (or other comparable references) to review the detailed information they offer on the content areas that were more difficult for you.

Finally, after having completed your review and preparation, you can retake the Practice Exam. By following the suggested strategies for dealing with your areas of weakness, you should see an improvement in your overall score as well as in your Performance Profile results.

7

Rationales for the Practice Exam

7

Rationales for the Practice Exam

1. Correct answer: 3

1. This question would be more relevant for initiating the care plan rather than updating it. Because the client has mid-stage Alzheimer's disease, it is unlikely that he will be going back home.
2. Children may have a different perspective and may not be client-centred.
3. **This information is critical in the development of a personalized care plan.**
4. This question is pertinent, but is not sufficient for updating a personalized daily care plan.

Classification

Cognitive Level: Application
Competency Category:
Foundations of practice

References

Lewis, S.L., et al. (2010), p. 53
Potter, P.A., Perry, A.G., Stockert, P., & Hall, A. (2011), p. 107

2. Correct answer: 4

1. This does not address the son's question about his father's daily care.
2. This does not address the son's question about his father's daily care.
3. This response does not encourage family participation.
4. **Often, family and friends are excellent for assisting clients with activities of daily living.**

Classification

Cognitive Level: Application
Competency Category:
Collaborative practice

References

Potter, P.A., Perry, A.G., Ross-Kerr, J.C., & Wood, M.J. (2009), p. 195
Rosdahl, C.B., & Kowalski, M.T. (2008), p. 358

3. Correct answer: 4

1. The client's condition must be assessed prior to moving him.
2. It is premature to call his wife. The client's condition must be assessed first.
3. Some falls result in serious injuries such as fractures and head trauma. Assessment must be completed first to rule out the need for urgent care interventions.
4. **The first action in any situation is to call for assistance immediately and remain with the client. Necessary care is dependent on an assessment.**

Classification

Cognitive Level: Critical Thinking
Competency Category:
Professional, ethical and legal practice

References

Potter, P.A., Perry, A.G., Ross-Kerr, J.C., & Wood, M.J. (2009), p. 140
Rosdahl, C.B., & Kowalski, M.T. (2008), pp. 467-468

4. Correct answer: 4

1. This breaches Mr. Robichaud's confidentiality because other care providers may not be involved in his care.
2. Although this might be a possible solution, there is no guarantee that the experienced peer will be available everyday. The additional care provider may also confuse Mr. Robichaud.
3. This approach does not identify Jeanne's underlying feelings regarding caring for people with Alzheimer's disease. In addition, Jeanne's discomfort may not be related to a lack of knowledge.
4. **Because the practical nurse's interpretation of Jeanne's non-verbal behaviour is subjective, it is important to validate its perceived meaning.**

Classification

Cognitive Level: Critical Thinking
Competency Category:
Collaborative practice

References

Berman, A., Snyder, S.J., Kozier, B., & Erb, G. (2008), p. 481
Potter, P.A., Perry, A.G., Ross-Kerr, J.C., & Wood, M.J. (2009), p. 250

5. Correct answer: 3

1. "Small" is a subjective term and can be interpreted differently. This entry does not fully describe all required aspects of the assessment.
2. Grapes come in different sizes and are not an exact form of measurement. This entry does not fully describe all required aspects of the assessment.
3. **This entry fully describes the assessment findings in objective, concise terms. Exact measurements promote accuracy.**
4. Use of the term "appears" is not acceptable because it suggests that the practical nurse did not know all the details related to the assessment. This entry does not fully describe all required aspects of the assessment.

Classification

Cognitive Level: Application
Competency Category:
Professional, ethical and legal practice

References

Kozier, B., et al. (2010), p. 943
Potter, P.A., Perry, A.G., Ross-Kerr, J.C., & Wood, M.J. (2009), pp. 212-213

6. Correct answer: 3

1. This action is ignoring the client's concern. When medications are questioned, it is important to re-check the physician's order.
2. Although this may be true, this action is ignoring the client's concern. When medications are questioned, it is important to re-check the physician's order.
3. **When medications are questioned, it is important to re-check the physician's order.**
4. The medication could have been transcribed incorrectly on the medication administration record (MAR) sheet. When medications are questioned, it is important to re-check the physician's order.

Classification

Cognitive Level: Application
Competency Category:
Foundations of practice

References

Kozier, B., et al. (2010), p. 815
Potter, P.A., Perry, A.G., Ross-Kerr, J.C., & Wood, M.J. (2009), pp. 693-694

7. Correct answer: 2

1. The lower leg is not one of the preferred sites as it often has hair. Transdermal patches should not be put on distal extremities.
2. **The upper arm is one of the recommended sites as it is a relatively clean and hairless area of the skin.**
3. The lumbar area is not one of the preferred sites because the patch may become contaminated or peel off.
4. The upper thigh is not one of the preferred sites because it often has hair.

Classification

Cognitive Level: Knowledge / Comprehension
Competency Category:
Foundations of practice

References

Clayton, B.D., Stock, Y.N., & Cooper, S.E. (2010), p. 403
CPS (2010), p. 1590

8. Correct answer: 4

1. The infusion must be maintained to keep the vein open for possible intravenous medications such as IV furosemide (Lasix).
2. The assessment findings are more indicative of fluid volume excess. Deep breathing and coughing exercises are therefore not appropriate.
3. The assessment findings indicate possible fluid volume excess. Maintaining the infusion rate at 150 mL / h will make the problem worse.
4. **Fluid volume excess is a complication of infusion therapy. The appropriate intervention is to notify the physician. In most cases, the physician will order a decrease in the rate of the infusion.**

Classification

Cognitive Level: Critical Thinking
Competency Category:
Foundations of practice

References

Craven, R.F., & Hirnle, C.J. (2009), p. 575
Ignatavicius, D.D., & Workman, M.L. (2010), p. 230

9. Correct answer: 3

1. Checking the blood glucose is important at some point but not a priority now. Checking the blood glucose level will not improve his respiration.
2. Checking the blood glucose is important at some point but not a priority now. Nitroglycerin is required to open the coronary arteries to increase the oxygen supply to the myocardium.
3. **It is important to assess vital signs prior to giving nitroglycerin because the medication will lower blood pressure. Oxygen is required because the client is reporting shortness of breath. This follows priority order of treatment first for airway, breathing and circulation.**
4. The warm blanket is not necessary. It is important to assess the client before administering oxygen.

Classification

Cognitive Level: Critical Thinking
Competency Category:
Foundations of practice

References

Ignatavicius, D.D., & Workman, M.L. (2010), p. 790
Lewis, S.L., et al. (2010), pp. 873-874

10. Correct answer: 3

1. This is not an appropriate option. The practical nurse should report vomiting even if it did not occur in the hospital.
2. This is not an appropriate option. The client cannot determine what information is documented.
3. **Ethics reflect values, morals and principles of right and wrong. The morality of delivering truthful information is more compelling than maintaining confidence with the client. The mental health delivery system can impose limits on clients' abilities to exercise their rights.**
4. This is a false reassurance and ignores the client's request to withhold information.

Classification

Cognitive Level: Application
Competency Category:
Professional, ethical and legal practice

References

Craven, R.F., & Hirnle, C.J. (2009), pp. 203, 332
Potter, P.A., Perry, A.G., Stockert, P., & Hall, A. (2011), p. 173

11. Correct answer: 4

1. Trust and honesty are crucial to the therapeutic relationship and searching Jenny's room in her absence is a breach of trust. The milieu needs to be therapeutic to have an effect on behaviour.
2. A barrier to communication may be introduced by directly asking the client about the missing items.
3. Objective and subjective data are appropriate for charting but suspicions should not be charted. In addition, a barrier to communication may be introduced by directly asking the client about the missing items.
4. **Raising the issue provides an opportunity for dialogue. Using a general lead may encourage the client to talk and indicate that the practical nurse is interested in hearing more. The practical nurse is not mistrusting the client or accusing. Documentation on the client chart needs to be done for legal reasons. The nursing care plan should also be updated.**

Classification

Cognitive Level: Application
Competency Category:
Professional, ethical and legal practice

References

Craven, R.F., & Hirnle, C.J. (2009), pp. 203, 332
Potter, P.A., Perry, A.G., Stockert, P., & Hall, A. (2011), p. 177

12. Correct answer: 3

1. The inclusion of the client in planning and implementation of an intervention leads to a greater likelihood of success.
2. Eating disorders are a manifestation of disordered thoughts. Daily attention to weight will encourage obsession regarding food. The emphasis should be on caloric intake, not weight gain.
3. **Wellness is the priority and individual self-concept is distorted; therefore the emphasis must be on adequate nutrition. Using problem-solving helps adolescents make choices, while keeping a journal allows for self-expression. Developing individualized care plans requires input from the client.**
4. This type of information is not necessarily presented in peer support groups.

Classification

Cognitive Level: Critical Thinking
Competency Category:
Foundations of practice

References

Ignatavicius, D.D., & Workman, M.L. (2010), p. 5
Potter, P.A., Perry, A.G., Stockert, P., & Hall, A. (2011), pp. 197-199

13. Correct answer: 4

1. The specimen must be kept in the refrigerator unless it is sent to the laboratory immediately.
2. The container must be sterile.
3. The sample should be taken before rinsing with mouthwash.
4. **Deep breathing and coughing help mobilize secretions.**

Classification

Cognitive Level: Knowledge / Comprehension
Competency Category:
Foundations of practice

References

Berman, A., Snyder, S.J., Kozier, B., & Erb, G. (2008), p. 816
Potter, P.A., Perry, A.G., Stockert, P., & Hall, A. (2011), p. 899

14. Correct answer: 2

1. His contacts may have an increased chance of contracting the disease due to prolonged exposure and closer proximity, but this is not the primary concern at this point.
2. **Compliance with the medication protocol increases the likelihood of a complete recovery. It is critical for survival and a subsequent cure of the disease.**
3. TB often leads to a state of malnourishment and a well-balanced diet may not be sufficient. This client needs to increase the intake of calories and protein to aid healing.
4. Hydration is important but not crucial to survival and cure of the disease.

Classification

Cognitive Level: Application
Competency Category:
Collaborative practice

References

Ignatavicius, D.D., & Workman, M.L. (2010), p. 670
Lewis, S.L., et al. (2010), p. 638

15. Correct answer: 1

1. **The path of transmission for TB is through airborne droplets. Therefore, the best protection is to wear a respiratory protection device.**
2. If gloves are worn, they need not be sterile.
3. Wearing a gown does not protect the practical nurse from inhaling airborne droplets.
4. These will not protect the practical nurse from airborne droplets.

Classification

Cognitive Level: Knowledge / Comprehension
Competency Category:
Foundations of practice

References

Ignatavicius, D.D., & Workman, M.L. (2010), p. 670
Potter, P.A., Perry, A.G., Ross-Kerr, J.C., & Wood, M.J. (2009), p. 657

16. Correct answer: 2

1. Renal failure will not increase the probability of this happening.
2. **Excess fluid volume is a concern in clients with renal failure.**
3. Renal failure will not increase the probability of this happening.
4. Urine is not produced by the kidneys. Therefore, urinary retention is not anticipated in clients with renal failure.

Classification

Cognitive Level: Knowledge / Comprehension
Competency Category:
Foundations of practice

References

Ignatavicius, D.D., & Workman, M.L. (2010), pp. 1617-1618
Lewis, S.L., et al. (2010), pp. 1277, 1284-1285

17. Correct answer: 4

1. This is not a side effect of iron. Yellowing of the sclera is a sign of liver failure.
2. This is not a side effect of iron.
3. This is not a side effect of iron. It can cause discolouration of teeth if taken in fluid form.
4. **Iron can cause darkening of the stool.**

Classification

Cognitive Level: Knowledge / Comprehension
Competency Category:
Foundations of practice

References

CPS (2010), pp. 1178-1179
Lewis, S.L., et al. (2010), p. 749

18. Correct answer: 3

1. Given Mrs. Azzu's intake and output, she is most likely exhibiting fluid retention. Inspiratory stridor bilaterally is not related to fluid retention.
2. Given Mrs. Azzu's intake and output, she is most likely exhibiting fluid retention. Fine crackles in the bases bilaterally are not related to fluid retention.
3. **Given Mrs. Azzu's intake and output, she is most likely exhibiting fluid retention. Coarse crackles indicate fluid retention.**
4. These are normal breath sounds and are unrelated to fluid retention.

Classification

Cognitive Level: Application
Competency Category:
Foundations of practice

References

Ignatavicius, D.D., & Workman, M.L. (2010), p. 1613
Lewis, S.L., et al. (2010), p. 1284
Potter, P.A., Perry, A.G., Ross-Kerr, J.C., & Wood, M.J. (2009), p. 182

19. Correct answer: 1

1. **A potassium level of 6 mmol/L is high. Since oranges are high in potassium, Mrs. Azzu should avoid drinking orange juice.**
2. Green beans are low in potassium. There is no need to avoid this food.
3. Breads are low in potassium. There is no need to avoid this food.
4. Pineapple is low in potassium. There is no need to avoid this food.

Classification

Cognitive Level: Application
Competency Category:
Collaborative practice

References

Ignatavicius, D.D., & Workman, M.L. (2010), p. 1615
Lewis, S.L., et al. (2010), p. 1290

20. Correct answer: 4

1. It has not been determined that pain is the reason for his refusal.
2. It would be appropriate to determine the reason for refusal first. It may not be an issue of timing.
3. This response demonstrates a lack of empathy by the practical nurse toward Mr. Lemay.
4. **The practical nurse must determine the factors contributing to his refusal before planning treatment.**

Classification

Cognitive Level: Application
Competency Category:
Foundations of practice

References

Kozier, B., et al. (2010), p. 445
Lewis, S.L., et al. (2010), p. 73

21. Correct answer: 4

1. Elevating the leg may change the alignment of his femur.
2. This is not an appropriate action and will not remedy the bleeding.
3. A pressure dressing may inhibit circulation or may displace the alignment of the femur.
4. **By tracing the outline, the progression of bleeding can be determined.**

Classification

Cognitive Level: Application
Competency Category:
Foundations of practice

References

Ignatavicius, D.D., & Workman, M.L. (2010), p. 292
Lewis, S.L., et al. (2010), p. 445

22. Correct answer: 3

1. This can cause pressure/compression in the axillary area.
2. The unaffected leg should be placed on the step first.
3. **All the weight should be placed on the healthy leg and the crutches, while leaving the hand on the affected side free to support movement.**
4. A good shoe with a non-slip sole should be used to avoid slips.

Classification

Cognitive Level: Application
Competency Category:
Collaborative practice

References

Kozier, B., et al. (2010), pp. 1155-1159
Potter, P.A., Perry, A.G., Ross-Kerr, J.C., & Wood, M.J. (2009), pp. 1209-1212

23. Correct answer: 2

1. A hospital waiting room is typically crowded and busy. There would be little privacy provided for the clients to receive information or express their emotions.
2. **The environment should allow for as much privacy as possible with no distractions or noise.**
3. This environment may not be appropriate depending on the family's religious beliefs. This is also a common area that is used by other clients and may not offer sufficient privacy.
4. It is not appropriate to provide updates in front of the client, especially when the client is a young child.

Classification

Cognitive Level: Application
Competency Category:
Collaborative practice

References

Kozier, B., et al. (2010), pp. 420-422
Potter, P.A., Perry, A.G., Ross-Kerr, J.C., & Wood, M.J. (2009), p. 209

24. Correct answer: 3

1. This may not be helpful at this time. The practical nurse must first address the family's concerns.
2. This may not be helpful at this time. Providing literature does not ensure that the family will understand the information provided by the physician.
3. **It is important to provide clear, up-to-date, relevant information and explanations throughout treatment.**
4. A social worker may provide the needed support, but will not be able to clarify the physician's information.

Classification

Cognitive Level: Application
Competency Category:
Professional, ethical and legal practice

References

Hockenberry, M.J., & Wilson, D. (2011), p. 12
Potter, P.A., Perry, A.G., Ross-Kerr, J.C., & Wood, M.J. (2009), pp. 304-306

25. Correct answer: 3

1. Excessive elevation of the syringe can cause the feeding to flow too quickly and result in an increased risk of aspiration.
2. Using the plunger can also cause the feeding to flow too quickly and result in an increased risk of aspiration.
3. **Flushing with a small amount of water can dilute the feeding and unclog the tubing.**
4. Reinserting the tubing would not be part of the practical nurse's scope of practice.

Classification

Cognitive Level: Application
Competency Category:
Professional, ethical and legal practice

References

Ignatavicius, D.D., & Workman, M.L. (2010), p. 1398
Kozier, B., et al. (2010), pp. 1217-1218

26. Correct answer: 3

1. Participating in end-of-life care allows for closure and facilitates a healthy grieving process.
2. This may not be the most appropriate solution. Whenever possible, the family should participate in end-of-life care.
3. **Participating in end-of-life care allows for closure and facilitates a healthy grieving process. As a result, the needs of the family should be considered by the interprofessional health-care team.**
4. Although this may be helpful, this action on its own denies the family's right to be involved in the decision-making around the care provided to Emily.

Classification

Cognitive Level: Application
Competency Category:
Professional, ethical and legal practice

References

Hockenberry, M.J., & Wilson, D. (2011), p. 886
Potter, P.A., Perry, A.G., Ross-Kerr, J.C., & Wood, M.J. (2009), p. 468

27. Correct answer: 1

1. **Delayed capillary refill indicates inadequate vascular function. This may require immediate attention.**
2. These would be normal findings following a trauma such as the one experienced by Derek.
3. These findings are normal following a fractured left wrist.
4. Some foot pain is normal following a femur fracture.

Classification

Cognitive Level: Application
Competency Category:
Foundations of practice

References

Kozier, B., et al. (2010), p. 616
Lewis, S.L., et al. (2010), pp. 807, 1746

28. Correct answer: 4

1. There is no known correlation between wrist fractures and the development of fat emboli.
2. Diet has not been identified as a factor in the development of fat emboli.
3. Dehydration is not a known factor in the development of fat emboli.
4. **Fat globules move into the blood from bone marrow in fractured long bones such as the femur.**

Classification

Cognitive Level: Knowledge/Comprehension
Competency Category:
Foundations of practice

References

Ignatavicius, D.D., & Workman, M.L. (2010), p. 1182
Lewis, S.L., et al. (2010), pp. 807, 1753

29. Correct answer: 2

1. The cast on Derek's left wrist will make this difficult.
2. **This will increase lung expansion and decrease the risk of respiratory complications.**
3. Given his fractured ribs, it is unlikely that Derek will be able to turn frequently from side to side.
4. His fractured wrist and ribs will make this very painful.

Classification

Cognitive Level: Application
Competency Category:
Foundations of practice

References

Kozier, B., et al. (2010), p. 1335
Lewis, S.L., et al. (2010), p. 436

30. Correct answer: 1

1. **Documentation is based on evidence. This is clear, concise and meets legal requirements.**
2. The term "inappropriate behaviour" is subjective and not suitable for documentation purposes.
3. This documentation is not evidence-based and not appropriate.
4. It is not appropriate to say that "the client is dirty" when documenting.

Classification

Cognitive Level: Application
Competency Category:
Professional, ethical and legal practice

References

Craven, R.F., & Hirnle, C.J. (2009), p. 205
Kozier, B., et al. (2010), pp. 487-489

31. Correct answer: 1

1. **This uses an interprofessional approach when advocating for Mr. Spencer. The social worker may also be able to assist the client with his housing needs.**
2. This is a breach of confidentiality and is not appropriate.
3. This does not address Mr. Spencer's mental health needs.
4. This is not advocating for the client and would not address Mr. Spencer's long-term mental health needs.

Classification

Cognitive Level: Application
Competency Category:
Professional, ethical and legal practice

References

Kozier, B., et al. (2010), pp. 84-85
Potter, P.A., Perry, A.G., Ross-Kerr, J.C., & Wood, M.J. (2010), pp. 92-93

32. Correct answer: 4

1. Telling a client that his behaviour is inappropriate is not professional or helpful.
2. It has not been stated that the noises he is hearing are voices.
3. This is not a professional interaction and may be perceived as threatening by the client.
4. **Too many issues brought forth at the same time will overwhelm the client. As a result, it is preferable to bring forward the priority issues first.**

Classification

Cognitive Level: Application
Competency Category:
Foundations of practice

References

Arnold, E.C., & Undeman Boggs, K. (2007), p. 391
Craven, R.F., & Hirnle, C.J. (2009), p. 1261

33. Correct answer: 3

1. Given Mr. Spencer's manifestations, immediate hospitalization would be premature.
2. This is not addressing Mr. Spencer's long-term mental health needs.
3. **This option is appropriate because the practical nurse is advocating for the client. By increasing visits, the client could maintain stability. A psychiatric assessment may be necessary.**
4. This is not consistent with building the nurse-client relationship and may be perceived by the client as a threat.

Classification

Cognitive Level: Critical Thinking
Competency Category:
Foundations of practice

References

Kozier, B., et al. (2010), pp. 84-85
Potter, P.A., Perry, A.G., Ross-Kerr, J.C., & Wood, M.J. (2010), pp. 165-166

34. Correct answer: 4

1. Gravida 2, para 3 refers to a second pregnancy and three viable births. Mrs. Proud would have had to have twins plus another birth past 20 weeks.
2. Gravida 2, para 2 refers to a second pregnancy and two viable births.
3. Gravida 3, para 2 refers to a third pregnancy with two viable births prior to this delivery.
4. **Accurate method of recording obstetrical history for a third pregnancy and one viable birth.**

Classification

Cognitive Level: Application
Competency Category:
Professional, ethical and legal practice

References

Lowdermilk, D., Perry, S.E., & Cashion, M.C. (2011), pp. 169-170
Pillitteri, A. (2010), p. 253

35. Correct answer: 4

1. The cervix dilates up to 3-4 cm in this stage.
2. Newborn is delivered at this stage.
3. Cervix is fully dilated at this stage.
4. **This is the first stage of labour just prior to full dilation.**

Classification

Cognitive Level: Knowledge/Comprehension
Competency Category:
Foundations of practice

References

Lowdermilk, D., Perry, S.E., & Cashion, M.C. (2011), pp. 342
Pillitteri, A. (2010), p. 360-362

36. Correct answer: 3

1. This is not an accurate conclusion from the above data. The Apgar score would be higher.
2. This is not an accurate conclusion from the above data. The Apgar score would be higher.
3. **One point would be subtracted from the 10-point Apgar assessment because of the acrocyanosis.**
4. This is not an accurate conclusion from the above data. The Apgar score would be lower.

Classification

Cognitive Level: Application
Competency Category:
Foundations of practice

References

Lowdermilk, D., Perry, S.E., & Cashion, M.C. (2011), pp. 479-480
Pillitteri, A. (2010), pp. 467-468

37. Correct answer: 1

1. **The clinical manifestations are suggestive of a full bladder.**
2. Clinical manifestations suggest a full bladder. There is no reported pain or discomfort.
3. It is not necessary to notify the physician at this time.
4. It is important to allow the client to void first.

Classification

Cognitive Level: Critical Thinking
Competency Category:
Foundations of practice

References

Lowdermilk, D., Perry, S.E., & Cashion, M.C. (2011), p. 388
Pillitteri, A. (2010), p. 424

38. Correct answer: 3

1. If colon cancer is suspected, a lower GI series or colonoscopy is needed. An upper GI series would not be helpful.
2. A colposcopy is used to view the uterus. An occult blood test is not required in this case.
3. **A colonoscopy is used to view the rectum and to diagnose rectal cancer. In addition, hemoglobin levels should be monitored because of the blood loss.**
4. Creatinine is used to assess kidney function and is not relevant if colorectal cancer is suspected.

Classification

Cognitive Level: Application
Competency Category:
Foundations of practice

References

Ignatavicius, D.D., & Workman, M.L. (2010), pp. 1295-1296
Lewis, S.L., et al. (2010), p. 1010

39. Correct answer: 2

1. A stoma that is bluish in colour is a medical emergency.
2. **A bluish stoma is an emergency and the client will probably be returning to the operating room.**
3. A stoma that is bluish in colour is a medical emergency and needs to be dealt with immediately.
4. A stoma that is bluish in colour is a medical emergency and needs to be dealt with immediately.

Classification

Cognitive Level: Application
Competency Category:
Foundations of practice

References

Ignatavicius, D.D., & Workman, M.L. (2010), pp. 1299-1300
Lewis, S.L., et al. (2010), p. 1148

40. Correct answer: 3

1. This is providing false reassurance.
2. This is a leading question.
3. **This addresses his concerns with an open-ended question.**
4. This is avoiding the issue.

Classification

Cognitive Level: Application
Competency Category:
Collaborative practice

References

Arnold, E.C., & Undeman Boggs, K. (2007), p. 207
Craven, R.F., & Hirnle, C.J. (2009), pp. 336-337

41. Correct answer: 3

1. A liquid stool would be found in an ascending colostomy.
2. A semi-formed stool would be found in a transverse colostomy.
3. **A descending colostomy produces increasingly solid fecal drainage. Stool from a sigmoid ostomy are normal of formed consistency.**
4. There may be absent bowel sounds for several days after surgery, but eventually bowel sounds will return and he will produce solid stool.

Classification

Cognitive Level: Critical Thinking
Competency Category:
Collaborative practice

References

Kozier, B., et al. (2010), pp. 1234-1235
Lewis, S.L., et al. (2010), p. 1147

42. Correct answer: 4

1. The NG output is abnormally high and the physician would need to be notified immediately.
2. This defers responsibility and is not necessary.
3. The NG output is abnormally high and the physician would need to be notified immediately.
4. **This NG output is abnormally high. The physician would need to be notified. The physician would probably order electrolytes and the replacement of lost fluids.**

Classification

Cognitive Level: Critical Thinking
Competency Category:
Foundations of practice

References

Kozier, B., et al. (2010), pp. 1383-1384
Lewis, S.L., et al. (2010), p. 1139

43. Correct answer: 2

1. The medication calculation is incorrect.
2. **The medication calculation is correct.**
3. The medication calculation is incorrect.
4. The medication calculation is incorrect.

Classification

Cognitive Level: Application
Competency Category:
Foundations of practice

References

Kozier, B., et al. (2010), pp. 811-812
Potter, P.A., Perry, A.G., Ross-Kerr, J.C., & Wood, M.J. (2010), p. 686

44. Correct answer: 2

1. Cleansing in this direction may introduce organisms into the wound.
2. **Cleansing in this direction may prevent the introduction of organisms into the wound.**
3. Cleansing in this direction may introduce organisms into the wound.
4. Cleansing in this direction may introduce organisms into the wound.

Classification

Cognitive Level: Knowledge/Comprehension
Competency Category:
Foundations of practice

References

Kozier, B., et al. (2010), p. 1048
Potter, P.A., Perry, A.G., Ross-Kerr, J.C., & Wood, M.J. (2010), p. 1272

45. Correct answer: 2

1. While wearing gloves adheres to standard precautions, elevating the extremity would be less helpful than applying pressure.
2. **Wearing gloves adheres to standard precautions and allows the practical nurse to provide client care. Direct pressure is the best option.**
3. If applying pressure to the site, it is important that the practical nurse wear gloves. Notifying the nurse-in-charge is not an immediate priority.
4. It is important to maintain standard precautions by wearing gloves. Direct pressure to the IV site is also necessary.

Classification

Cognitive Level: Critical Thinking
Competency Category:
Foundations of practice

References

Ignatavicius, D.D., & Workman, M.L. (2010), p. 446
Lewis, S.L., et al. (2010), pp. 296-297

46. Correct answer: 3

1. This does not follow the proper assessment sequence.
2. This does not follow the proper assessment sequence.
3. **This is the first step in the client assessment process.**
4. This does not follow the proper assessment sequence.

Classification

Cognitive Level: Critical Thinking
Competency Category:
Foundations of practice

References

Lewis, S.L., et al. (2010), p. 10
Potter, P.A., Perry, A.G., Ross-Kerr, J.C., & Wood, M.J. (2010), p. 165

47. Correct answer: 4

1. The formula is mL/h multiplied by the number of hours.
2. The formula is mL/h multiplied by the number of hours.
3. The formula is mL/h multiplied by the number of hours.
4. **The formula is mL/h multiplied by the number of hours. Therefore, 125 mL × 24 h = 3,000 mL.**

Classification

Cognitive Level: Application
Competency Category:
Foundations of practice

References

Kozier, B., et al. (2010), pp. 1411-1412
Potter, P.A., Perry, A.G., Ross-Kerr, J.C., & Wood, M.J. (2010), p. 970

48. Correct answer: 1

1. **In order to properly assess for a transfusion reaction, it is critical to have baseline vital signs before giving blood.**
2. D5W should not be used to prime the blood administration set. Normal saline should be used.
3. There is no need to verify this order.
4. This is not necessary. The cart does not need to be in the room.

Classification

Cognitive Level: Critical Thinking
Competency Category:
Foundations of practice

References

Ignatavicius, D.D., & Workman, M.L. (2010), pp. 918-919
Kozier, B., et al. (2010), pp. 1422-1424

49. Correct answer: 3

1. Taking the client's hand may put him off balance.
2. This may encourage dependence.
3. **Give the client a choice to promote maximum independence.**
4. This may put undue stress on the wife.

Classification

Cognitive Level: Application
Competency Category:
Collaborative practice

References

Lewis, S.L., et al. (2010), p. 98
Potter, P.A., Perry, A.G., Ross-Kerr, J.C., & Wood, M.J. (2010), pp. 364-365

50. Correct answer: 3

1. This will not provide a reliable indication of what Joan has eaten. Joan could have discarded unwanted food in the practical nurse's absence.
2. The dynamics of this illness preclude relying on Joan for an accurate record of her food intake.
3. **This provides the most accurate and objective data related to food intake.**
4. This will not provide a reliable indication of what Joan has eaten. Joan could have discarded unwanted food in the practical nurse's absence.

Classification

Cognitive Level: Application
Competency Category:
Foundations of practice

References

Austin, W., & Boyd, M.A. (2010), p. 504
Ball, W., Bindler, J., & Cowen, K. (2010), p. 305

51. Correct answer: 2

1. Joan will be more likely to experience hypothermia.
2. **Joan is likely to exhibit a hypothyroid-like state manifested by dry skin.**
3. Lanugo (baby-like fine hair) of the face, extremities and trunk may occur. Coarse hair will not occur.
4. Joan will be more likely to experience hypotension than hypertension.

Classification

Cognitive Level: Knowledge / Comprehension
Competency Category:
Foundations of practice

References

Austin, W., & Boyd, M.A. (2010), p. 492
Ignatavicius, D.D., & Workman, M.L. (2010), p. 1392

52. Correct answer: 3

1. This is a non-therapeutic response. Standing side by side in front of a mirror will not convince Joan that her thighs are not fat.
2. While somewhat empathetic, this response is not reflective of honesty and does not reinforce trust in the relationship established with the practical nurse.
3. **This truthful response will reinforce the trust established in the relationship. It is honest and demonstrates warmth, and is an effective approach to therapeutic dialogue.**
4. This non-therapeutic response would reinforce negative thinking and coping strategies.

Classification

Cognitive Level: Critical Thinking
Competency Category:
Collaborative practice

References

Austin, W., & Boyd, M.A. (2010), p. 502
Townsend, M. (2009), p. 133

53. Correct answer: 3

1. While Joan's perception is that she is making progress, her actions indicate otherwise.
2. The practical nurse should participate fully and provide accurate and objective information regarding Joan's progress. While Joan's perception is that she is making progress, her actions indicate otherwise.
3. **This is a therapeutic approach to assist her to develop insight into her condition. While Joan's perception is that she is making progress, her actions indicate otherwise.**
4. Discharge planning should have begun at the initial interprofessional conference. It is not optimal to begin discharge planning at this point.

Classification

Cognitive Level: Critical Thinking
Competency Category:
Collaborative practice

References

Austin, W., & Boyd, M.A. (2010), p. 125
Potter, P.A., & Perry, A.G., Ross-Kerr, J.C., & Wood, M.J. (2010), p. 259

54. Correct answer: 3

1. Familiarizing Mrs. Hart with the unit is a standard way to reduce anxiety, but emotional concerns are more important.
2. A back rub is one way to reduce anxiety, but it is not the most appropriate approach to take upon admission.
3. **The need for emotional support is particularly strong for clients undergoing breast cancer surgery. Listening to her concerns is therefore optimal upon admission.**
4. Journaling is valuable but takes time. Listening to her concerns instead would address her immediate concerns and anxiety.

Classification

Cognitive Level: Application
Competency Category:
Collaborative practice

References

Kozier, B., et al. (2010), p. 399
Potter, P.A., Perry, A.G., Ross-Kerr, J.C., & Wood, M.J. (2010), p. 257

55. Correct answer: 3

1. The first postoperative day is too soon to be passing flatus.
2. Deep breathing exercises should be done more often than every 4 hours.
3. **Hemorrhage is a postoperative risk and should be assessed on the first postoperative day.**
4. The first postoperative day is too soon to begin wall-walking exercises.

Classification

Cognitive Level: Critical Thinking
Competency Category:
Foundations of practice

References

Ignatavicius, D.D., & Workman, M.L. (2010), p. 286
Kozier, B., et al. (2010), p. 1039

56. Correct answer: 1

1. **The affected arm should be used for exercise. Encouraging Mrs. Hart to brush her hair using her hand on the affected side promotes independence.**
2. It is inappropriate to suggest to a client with a body image disturbance to avoid viewing the affected area.
3. Psychologically, it is better for breast cancer clients to wear their own clothing as soon as possible.
4. The practical nurse should allow Mrs. Hart to perform her own perineal care as it encourages independence and helps to enhance self-esteem.

Classification

Cognitive Level: Application
Competency Category:
Foundations of practice

References

Day, R., Paul, P., Williams, B., Smeltzer, S.C., & Bare, B. (2007), p. 1478
Ignatavicius, D.D., & Workman, M.L. (2010), p. 1679

57. Correct answer: 1

1. **A full chest assessment should be done prior to reporting the findings.**
2. Mrs. Mayhew requires further assessment. Currently, there is nothing to indicate a change in condition.
3. A full chest assessment should be done prior to reporting the findings.
4. Further assessment is required prior to documenting the practical nurse's findings.

Classification

Cognitive Level: Critical Thinking
Competency Category:
Foundations of practice

References

Hall, A. (2011), p. 78
Kozier, B., et al. (2010), p. 85
Potter, P.A., Perry, A.G., Stockert, P., & Hall, A. (2010), p. 78

58. Correct answer: 4

1. This would not promote increased lung expansion.
2. Placing both arms on pillows would not promote comfort as effectively as allowing her to choose a comfortable position.
3. This may compromise her breathing.
4. **Leaning forward would promote increased lung expansion.**

Classification

Cognitive Level: Application
Competency Category:
Collaborative practice

References

Ignatavicius, D.D., & Workman, M.L. (2010), p. 624
Taylor, C.R., Lillis, C., Lemone, P., & Lynn, P. (2008), p. 162

59. Correct answer: 3

1. Brush should be held horizontally and dentures should be brushed using a back and forth motion.
2. Hot water could damage the dentures.
3. **Warm water dilutes particles and rinses dentures more effectively without damaging the dentures.**
4. Hard-bristled toothbrushes may damage the dentures.

Classification

Cognitive Level: Knowledge / Comprehension
Competency Category:
Collaborative practice

References

Potter, P.A., Perry, A.G., Ross-Kerr, J.C., & Wood, M.J. (2010), p. 864
Taylor, C.R., Lillis, C., Lemone, P., & Lynn, P. (2008), pp. 1141-1142

60. Correct answer: 1

1. **Accuracy requires the practical nurse to be specific and definite.**
2. The chart is about the individual client. For proper charting, the subject of the sentence is omitted.
3. "Well" is a subjective term, and as a result, this charting would contain non-objective data.
4. This statement is too vague for use in a client's chart.

Classification

Cognitive Level: Application
Competency Category:
Professional, ethical and legal practice

References

Potter, P.A., Perry, A.G., Ross-Kerr, J.C., & Wood, M.J. (2010), p. 212
Taylor, C.R., Lillis, C., Lemone, P., & Lynn, P. (2008), p. 356

61. Correct answer: 1

1. **This would allow the client to be active within the limits of her tolerance.**
2. This is vague and may be an unrealistic goal.
3. She may be able to do small tasks but the housework would be too demanding to do all at once. She should work at own pace.
4. This puts her at high risk of infections.

Classification

Cognitive Level: Critical Thinking
Competency Category:
Foundations of practice

References

Day, R.A., Paul, P., Williams, B., Smeltzer, S.C., & Bare, B. (2007), pp. 580-581
Ignatavicius, D.D., & Workman, M.L. (2010), p. 633

62. Correct answer: 2

1. This is dismissive of the daughter's concerns and does not provide emotional support.
2. **This is a therapeutic response which provides appropriate health teaching and a rationale for why the daughter needs to wear a mask.**
3. This is false reassurance. In addition, this response could create fear.
4. The issue is not about hearing; it is one of protection and facilitating communication. This is not a therapeutic response.

Classification

Cognitive Level: Application
Competency Category:
Foundations of practice

References

Ignatavicius, D.D., & Workman, M.L. (2010), pp. 4, 447
Potter, P.A., Perry, A.G., Ross-Kerr, J.C., & Wood, M.J. (2010), pp. 286-287, 657

63. Correct answer: 4

1. This is not the best option because the only universal sign/body language is the smile and other gestures may be misinterpreted.
2. The family member could be caught up in the crisis and may not accurately convey the message. It is also a confidentiality issue.
3. This defers the responsibility of getting blood work in a timely manner.
4. **Professional interpreters are better at communicating medical terms and would reduce the risk of breaches in client privacy and confidentiality.**

Classification

Cognitive Level: Critical Thinking
Competency Category:
Professional, ethical and legal practice

References

Balzer Riley, J. (2008), p. 53
Potter, P.A., Perry, A.G., Ross-Kerr, J.C., & Wood, M.J. (2010), pp. 255, 261

64. Correct answer: 3

1. This does not address the respiratory status as the first step (ABCs).
2. This does not address the respiratory status as the first step (ABCs).
3. **The priority should be to complete a focused respiratory assessment (ABCs).**
4. This does not address the respiratory status as the first step (ABCs).

Classification

Cognitive Level: Critical Thinking
Competency Category:
Foundations of practice

References

Potter, P.A., Perry, A.G., Ross-Kerr, J.C., & Wood, M.J. (2010), p. 541
Taylor, C.R., Lillis, C., Lemone, P., & Lynn, P. (2008), p. 248

65. Correct answer: 3

1. Dehydration due to hyperthermia is not the most likely explanation in this situation.
2. This is part of an agglutination test that confirms immunity to diseases. It is not the most likely explanation of an elevated WBC count.
3. **An elevation in the number and type of WBCs indicates a possible infectious process.**
4. This is not indicated by an elevated WBC count.

Classification

Cognitive Level: Application
Competency Category:
Foundations of practice

References

Potter, P.A., Perry, A.G., Ross-Kerr, J.C., & Wood, M.J. (2010), p. 165
Timby, B.K., & Smith, N.E. (2007), p. 196

66. Correct answer: 3

1. Although written discharge instructions are provided, it does not answer the question.
2. It is the practical nurse's responsibility to provide discharge instructions.
3. **Adherence to the prescribed treatment regimen is very important and can lead to a cure.**
4. It is the practical nurse's responsibility to provide discharge instructions before the client leaves the unit.

Classification

Cognitive Level: Application
Competency Category:
Foundations of practice

References

Ignatavicius, D.D., & Workman, M.L. (2010), p. 670
Lewis, S.L., et al. (2010), p. 638

67. Correct answer: 3

1. A client with splints may not be able to use a bedpan. In addition, client consent must be obtained before applying the splints.
2. This position does not allow for proper splint application. In addition, client consent must be obtained before applying the splints.
3. **Consent must be obtained prior to any procedure or treatment.**
4. This position does not allow for proper splint application. In addition, client consent must be obtained before applying the splints.

Classification

Cognitive Level: Application
Competency Category:
Professional, ethical and legal practice

References

Kozier, B., et al. (2010), p. 97
Potter, P.A., Perry, A.G., Ross-Kerr, J.C., & Wood, M.J. (2010), pp. 98, 107-108

68. Correct answer: 2

1. This action is not the most helpful for clients with osteoarthritis because they still require assistance with positioning on the bedpan.
2. **Rolling takes less energy than lifting. Therefore, it is much easier for a client with arthritis. In addition, the fracture bedpan is more comfortable for the client to use due to its shallow depth.**
3. High-Fowler's position is too high for this client.
4. Leaving a client with arthritis on the bedpan for 15 minutes could promote joint discomfort and pain. The practical nurse must ensure that the call bell is accessible and instruct the client to ring as soon as she is finished.

Classification

Cognitive Level: Application
Competency Category:
Collaborative practice

References

Kozier, B., et al. (2010), pp. 1244-1245
Potter, P.A., Perry, A.G., Ross-Kerr, J.C., & Wood, M.J. (2010), pp. 1162-1163

69. Correct answer: 2

1. Clients with arthritis should be assessed for their fatigue level, not their motivational level, before initiating activities. The level of motivation does not address safety.
2. **Well-fitting, non-skid shoes lessen the risk of slipping during the transfer.**
3. Ms. O'Connor's feet should be placed 15 to 20 cm apart to provide a wide base of support.
4. This action will maintain good posture but will not promote safety during the transfer.

Classification

Cognitive Level: Application
Competency Category:
Foundations of practice

References

Potter, P.A., Perry, A.G., Ross-Kerr, J.C., & Wood, M.J. (2010), p. 815
Taylor, C.R., Lillis, C., Lemone, P., & Lynn, P. (2008), p. 1305

70. Correct answer: 4

1. A sitting position promotes self-care. However, it would not be the initial nursing action for active independence.
2. The practical nurse should not limit the time needed for morning care.
3. Although this action will strengthen self-care capacity and promote safety, it would not be the first priority.
4. **Assessing the client's capabilities and including the client's input would be the first priority in promoting active independence.**

Classification

Cognitive Level: Critical Thinking
Competency Category:
Foundations of practice

References

Lewis S.L., et al. (2010), p. 1806
Taylor, C.R., Lillis, C., Lemone, P., & Lynn, P. (2008), p. 180

71. Correct answer: 4

1. Before assessing for any psychiatric or possible mental health issues, physical reasons for confusion should be ruled out.
2. This could be done, but the Mini-Mental State Examination should be performed after a complete neurological assessment.
3. This could be done, but an assessment of medication side effects should be conducted after a complete neurological assessment.
4. **Part of the neurological assessment is the Glasgow Coma scale which includes orientation to person, place and time. Physical reasons for confusion should be ruled out.**

Classification

Cognitive Level: Critical Thinking
Competency Category:
Foundations of practice

References

Potter, P.A., Perry, A.G., Ross-Kerr, J.C., & Wood, M.J. (2010), pp. 541, 558
Taylor, C.R., Lillis, C., Lemone, P., & Lynn, P. (2008), p. 248

72. Correct answer: 2

1. Reviewing the client's intake/output is important, but is not the first action that should be taken before changing the IV container.
2. **Any time there is a break in the IV line, the physician's order should be checked.**
3. The physician's order should be checked prior to gathering the equipment.
4. The practical nurse should be aware of the physician's order before explaining the procedure to the client.

Classification

Cognitive Level: Critical Thinking
Competency Category:
Foundations of practice

References

Craven, R.F., & Hirnle, C.J. (2009), p. 598
Kozier, B., et al. (2010), p. 1416

73. Correct answer: 2

1. The bed should be raised to a comfortable working height for optimal body mechanics.
2. **This would promote client safety and should be done before starting the transfer.**
3. This would not be done first because the sling must be applied while the client is in supine position.
4. Only the side rail on the side that the lift is occurring should be lowered initially.

Classification

Cognitive Level: Application
Competency Category:
Collaborative practice

References

Craven, R.F., & Hirnle, C.J. (2009), p. 812
Potter, P.A., Perry, A.G., Ross-Kerr, J.C., & Wood, M.J. (2010), p. 815

74. Correct answer: 4

1. With cystitis, the client would be voiding small amounts of urine.
2. Dark brown urine indicates dehydration. With cystitis, the client would have cloudy urine.
3. An ammonia smell is a normal characteristic of urine.
4. **A client with cystitis goes to the washroom frequently. Voiding more often may also indicate incomplete emptying of the bladder or retention of urine.**

Classification

Cognitive Level: Application
Competency Category:
Foundations of practice

References

Craven, R.F., & Hirnle, C.J. (2009), p. 1081
Potter, P.A., Perry, A.G., Ross-Kerr, J.C., & Wood, M.J. (2010), p. 1102

75. Correct answer: 2

1. A client may report doing well to avoid bothering the practical nurse.
2. **A return demonstration is the best indication of learning.**
3. This shows the end result, not the procedure. In addition, someone else may have completed the appliance change.
4. This does not assess how well Mr. Hutmacher has learned to change his appliance.

Classification

Cognitive Level: Application
Competency Category:
Foundations of practice

References

Kozier, B., et al. (2010), pp. 531-532
Potter, P.A., Perry, A.G., Ross-Kerr, J.C., & Wood, M.J. (2010), p. 297

76. Correct answer: 4

1. Masks are not indicated for mouth care.
2. This would not be the initial step. Additionally, the mouth would be brushed with a soft toothbrush, not a denture brush.
3. It is not necessary to verify orders before providing mouth care.
4. **Gloves must be worn when in contact with mucous membranes and moist body substances.**

Classification

Cognitive Level: Application
Competency Category:
Foundations of practice

References

Kozier, B., et al. (2010), p. 732
Potter, P.A., Perry, A.G., Ross-Kerr, J.C., & Wood, M.J. (2010), pp. 657, 860

77. Correct answer: 4

1. The practical nurse needs to respect Mrs. Caron's right to self-determination, even though it may not be compatible with recommendations.
2. The practical nurse is not addressing the client's concerns.
3. The practical nurse is not addressing the client's concerns.
4. **The code of ethics indicates that a client's dignity must be preserved. Mrs. Caron's individual decision-making must be respected.**

Classification

Cognitive Level: Critical Thinking
Competency Category:
Professional, ethical and legal practice

References

Arnold, E.C., & Undeman Boggs, K. (2007), pp. 155-156
Potter, P.A., Perry, A.G., Ross-Kerr, J.C., & Wood, M.J. (2010), pp. 91-93

78. Correct answer: 3

1. This would be helpful, but the practical nurse should check the infusion control device rate first.
2. An infusion being delivered to a child requires a mini-drop administration set if an infusion control device is not attached. An infusion control device is in place in this case.
3. **This promotes the safe delivery of fluid at the correct rate.**
4. This may be necessary, but monitoring should be done more frequently.

Classification

Cognitive Level: Critical Thinking
Competency Category:
Foundations of practice

References

Hockenberry, M.J., & Wilson, D. (2011), p. 1071
Perry, S., Hockenberry, M., Lowdermilk, D., & Wilson, D. (2010), p. 1287

79. Correct answer: 2

1. The client should gently close his eyes. Squeezing would force the drops out of eye region.
2. **Pressing on the nasolacrimal duct prevents the medication from running out of the eye and down the duct, thus preventing systemic absorption.**
3. This is the wrong direction. The excess fluid should be wiped from the inner to the outer direction.
4. This is not required for eye drops.

Classification

Cognitive Level: Application
Competency Category:
Foundations of practice

References

Kozier, B., et al. (2010), p. 860
Potter, P.A., Perry, A.G., Ross-Kerr, J.C., & Wood, M.J. (2010), pp. 712-714

80. Correct answer: 3

1. This does not address the issue raised by the mother and does not provide health teaching.
2. This does not demonstrate the practical nurse's knowledge of precipitating factors for asthma and does not provide health teaching.
3. **The practical nurse confirms knowledge that cigarette smoke is a trigger for asthma. This acknowledges the mother's concerns and offers assistance with quitting.**
4. This is a judgmental answer, does not acknowledge the mother's concerns and does not offer support with quitting.

Classification

Cognitive Level: Critical Thinking
Competency Category:
Collaborative practice

References

Arnold, E.C., & Undeman Boggs, K. (2007), p. 367
Potter, P.A., Perry, A.G., Ross-Kerr, J.C., & Wood, M.J. (2010), pp. 300-302

81. Correct answer: 3

1. The muscle is too small to administer iron into.
2. Although a well-developed muscle, a deep IM injection may cause too much pain on a continuously used muscle.
3. **This muscle is the preferred site for IM injections, especially deep IM injections.**
4. Although this is a good muscle mass, it is not the recommended site for IM injections due to nerve and blood vessel proximity.

Classification

Cognitive Level: Application
Competency Category:
Foundations of practice

References

Kozier, B., et al. (2010), p. 842
Lehne, R.A. (2010), pp. 637-638

82. Correct answer: 2

1. A trapeze encourages spinal twisting by its location and would not assist the client to logroll.
2. **The use of a turning sheet to assist rolling in bed would best maintain spinal alignment.**
3. Trochanter rolls are used to prevent external rotation of the hip. They are not used for logrolling.
4. A sliding board will not assist with a turning action.

Classification

Cognitive Level: Application
Competency Category:
Professional, ethical and legal practice

References

Craven, R.F., & Hirnle, C.J. (2009), pp. 796-797
Potter, P.A., Perry, A.G., Ross-Kerr, J.C., & Wood, M.J. (2010), pp. 1219-1220

83. Correct answer: 2

1. Although the practical nurse would auscultate the client's chest at some point to confirm the circulatory overload, it is not the first action to be taken.
2. **The client is having an adverse blood reaction most likely because of circulatory overload. The circulatory volume is too high for the client's heart to manage. Therefore, the practical nurse does not want to further increase the circulating blood volume.**
3. This is not the priority. The infusion needs to be stopped immediately because the client is most likely experiencing circulatory overload.
4. Although other types of adverse reactions can include pyrexia, it is more likely that this client is experiencing circulatory overload. Therefore, stopping the administration of blood is the appropriate nursing action.

Classification

Cognitive Level: Critical Thinking
Competency Category:
Foundations of practice

References

Kozier, B., et al. (2010), p. 1420
Potter, P.A., Perry, A.G., Ross-Kerr, J.C., & Wood, M.J. (2010), pp. 979-982

84. Correct answer: 2

1. This amount is too low. Up to 1 mL can be injected.
2. **This is the maximum amount that can be injected subcutaneously without causing tissue damage.**
3. This amount is too large and may cause tissue damage.
4. This amount is too large and may cause tissue damage.

Classification

Cognitive Level: Knowledge / Comprehension
Competency Category:
Foundations of practice

References

Craven, R.F., & Hirnle, C.J. (2009), p. 524
Potter, P.A., Perry, A.G., Ross-Kerr, J.C., & Wood, M.J. (2010), pp. 730-731

85. Correct answer: 1

1. **Older clients who have difficulty with hearing or vision will often isolate themselves.**
2. The first step is to assess the client who is the primary information giver.
3. The first step is for the practical nurse to assess the client.
4. This is not a helpful intervention.

Classification

Cognitive Level: Critical Thinking
Competency Category:
Foundations of practice

References

Craven, R.F., & Hirnle, C.J. (2009), p. 1221
Potter, P.A., Perry, A.G., Ross-Kerr, J.C., & Wood, M.J. (2010), p. 1291

86. Correct answer: 3

1. This could be a medical emergency. As a result, the physician should be contacted first.
2. This could be a medical emergency. As a result, the physician should be contacted first.
3. **This could be a medical emergency. As a result, the physician should be contacted first.**
4. This could be a medical emergency. As a result, the physician should be contacted first.

Classification

Cognitive Level: Critical Thinking
Competency Category:
Foundations of practice

References

Perry, A.G., & Potter, P.A. (2010), p. 525
Potter, P.A., Perry, A.G., Ross-Kerr, J.C., & Wood, M.J. (2010), p. 691

87. Correct answer: 4

1. Sterile gloves are not needed to remove a dressing. Clean gloves would be sufficient.
2. There is no indication of an infection. Specimen collection is therefore not needed.
3. The incision line should be cleansed first.
4. **This precaution needs to be taken to avoid contamination with any wound drainage.**

Classification

Cognitive Level: Application
Competency Category:
Foundations of practice

References

Kozier, B., et al. (2010), p. 1047
Perry, A.G., & Potter, P.A. (2010), p. 1007

88. Correct answer: 1

1. **Sources of strength, meaning of life and life satisfaction are a reflection of spirituality.**
2. These reflect her education and cognitive level rather than her spiritual needs.
3. These are a reflection of psychosocial aspects of her life.
4. These are a reflection of her psychosocial profile.

Classification

Cognitive Level: Critical Thinking
Competency Category:
Foundations of practice

References

Arnold, E.C., & Undeman Boggs, K. (2007), p. 179
Craven, R.F., & Hirnle, C.J. (2009), p. 1327

89. Correct answer: 2

1. A client's response to the IV is not generally affected by activities such as moving in and out of bed.
2. **The IV flow rate may be altered by client activities such as moving in and out of bed.**
3. It is possible, but unlikely, that the IV needle would be dislodged by moving in and out of bed. It is much more likely for the flow rate to be altered.
4. It is possible, but unlikely, that the regulation clamp would be disturbed by moving in and out of bed. It is much more likely for the flow rate to be altered.

Classification

Cognitive Level: Application
Competency Category:
Foundations of practice

References

Kozier, B., et al. (2010), p. 1412
Perry, A.G., & Potter, P.A. (2010), p. 757

90. Correct answer: 1

1. **This prevents finding an empty bag without having a replacement bag available.**
2. This may not provide sufficient time to prepare the replacement solution before the container empties.
3. This may not provide sufficient time to prepare the replacement solution before the container empties.
4. This may not provide sufficient time to prepare the replacement solution before the container empties.

Classification

Cognitive Level: Knowledge/Comprehension
Competency Category:
Foundations of practice

References

Craven, R.F., & Hirnle, C.J. (2009), p. 598
Perry, A.G., & Potter, P.A. (2010), p. 762

91. Correct answer: 4

1. This is not always possible.
2. This could put the clients at risk if the workload is excessive.
3. This could be seen as abandonment. The practical nurse should address this issue with a supervisor.
4. **This is the first step in resolution of a conflict between beliefs and abilities to give care.**

Classification

Cognitive Level: Application
Competency Category:
Professional, ethical and legal practice

References

Kozier, B., et al. (2010), p. 77
Potter, P.A., Perry, A.G., Ross-Kerr, J.C., & Wood, M.J. (2010), p. 139

92. Correct answer: 4

1. This will not be helpful in regaining bladder control.
2. This may be appropriate but would not be the initial step.
3. Cranberry juice will not help bladder training.
4. **The client should be encouraged to void every 1 to 2 hours in the early stages of bladder retraining.**

Classification

Cognitive Level: Critical Thinking
Competency Category:
Collaborative practice

References

Ignatavicius, D.D., & Workman, M.L. (2010), p. 1567
Potter, P.A., Perry, A.G., Ross-Kerr, J.C., & Wood, M.J. (2010), p. 1138

93. Correct answer: 3

1. Although the physician should be informed, the IV must be slowed first.
2. A change of position would not address the cause of fluid overload.
3. **The client is manifesting signs of fluid overload. The IV must be slowed to prevent a worsening of the client's condition.**
4. This is not the first priority.

Classification

Cognitive Level: Critical Thinking
Competency Category:
Foundations of practice

References

Craven, R.F., & Hirnle, C.J. (2009), pp. 575-576
Potter, P.A., Perry, A.G., Ross-Kerr, J.C., & Wood, M.J. (2010), pp. 958-959

94. Correct answer: 3

1. More client information is required to correctly identify the correct blood recipient.
2. This would increase the potential for error in administration of the wrong units of blood to both clients. This may also be contrary to agency policy.
3. **It is advisable that blood should be transported to only one client at a time. This decreases the potential for life-threatening errors.**
4. There is no rationale for returning the blood immediately to the laboratory.

Classification

Cognitive Level: Critical Thinking
Competency Category:
Foundations of practice

References

Lewis, S.L., et al. (2010), pp. 274-276
Potter, P.A., Perry, A.G., Ross-Kerr, J.C., & Wood, M.J. (2010), pp. 981-982

95. Correct answer: 4

1. This would not be an initial action.
2. This action may not be appropriate.
3. This would be done after ensuring a patent airway.
4. **Adequate oxygen supply is essential to life and is always the first consideration in any assessment.**

Classification

Cognitive Level: Critical Thinking
Competency Category:
Foundations of practice

References

Ignatavicius, D.D., & Workman, M.L. (2010), p. 136
Lewis, S.L., et al. (2010), pp. 1926-1927

96. Correct answer: 2

1. The client from the operating room needs an immediate assessment.
2. **The client from the operating room should be assessed immediately for postoperative risks.**
3. The client from the operating room needs an immediate assessment.
4. The client from the operating room needs an immediate assessment. The client requiring pain medication would be seen next.

Classification

Cognitive Level: Critical Thinking
Competency Category:
Foundations of practice

References

Ignatavicius, D.D., & Workman, M.L. (2010), p. 289
Lewis, S.L., et al. (2010), pp. 446-447

97. Correct answer: 3

1. Adequate oxygenation is always the first consideration. The client should be given oxygen first.
2. Adequate oxygenation is always the first consideration. The client should be given oxygen first.
3. **The practical nurse can administer 1-2 L/min of oxygen autonomously. Adequate oxygenation is always the first consideration.**
4. Adequate oxygenation is always the first consideration. The client should be given oxygen first.

Classification

Cognitive Level: Critical Thinking
Competency Category:
Foundations of practice

References

Ignatavicius, D.D., & Workman, M.L. (2010), p. 638
Lewis, S.L., et al. (2010), p. 701

98. Correct answer: 3

1. There is no indication that legal guardianship is in place. The client can make her own decisions.
2. There is no indication that legal guardianship is in place. The client can make her own decisions.
3. **There is no indication that Mrs. Bates is not competent to make own decisions. Clients with early stage Alzheimer's disease can still retain decision-making skills.**
4. There is no indication that legal guardianship is in place. The client can make her own decisions.

Classification

Cognitive Level: Application
Competency Category:
Professional, ethical and legal practice

References

Lewis, S.L., et al. (2010), p. 1677
Potter, P.A., Perry A.G., Ross-Kerr, J.C., & Wood, M.J. (2009), pp. 98, 108

99. Correct answer: 3

1. This would be dependent on postoperative physician's order and would not be done initially.
2. It is not known if client will have an ostomy.
3. **After any surgery, clients have a reduced lung volume and need greater efforts to breathe. Deep breathing exercises will improve Mr. Ross' ability to cough and breathe.**
4. There are no specific restrictions associated with this surgery.

Classification

Cognitive Level:
Knowledge/Comprehension
Competency Category:
Collaborative practice

References

Ignatavicius, D.D., & Workman, M.L. (2010), p. 255
Lewis, S.L., et al. (2010), p. 404

100. Correct answer: 4

1. Driving may be hazardous. The practical nurse should first inquire about Mrs. Gore's planned means of transportation.
2. Irrigation with sterile water would not address Mrs. Gore's sensitivity to light.
3. It may take longer than 15 minutes for light sensitivity to resolve.
4. **Mrs. Gore will have altered vision due to the mydriatic medication. For safety reasons, she should not drive.**

Classification

Cognitive Level: Application
Competency Category: Foundations of practice

References

Clayton, B.D., Stock Y.N., & Cooper, S.E. (2010), p. 682
Lehne, R.A. (2010), p. 1223

101. Correct answer: 2

1. The practical nurse has taken no ownership of the problem.
2. **This approach is assertive and places responsibility for the problem with the right person.**
3. This is an avoidance strategy and not an attempt at resolution.
4. This is not the best initial response.

Classification

Cognitive Level: Critical Thinking
Competency Category: Collaborative practice

References

Kozier, B., et al. (2010), p. 407
Potter, P.A., Perry, A.G., Ross-Kerr, J.C., & Wood, M.J. (2009), pp. 136-137

102. Correct answer: 4

1. Sheepskin is used to prevent skin breakdown but will not prevent the external rotation of a limb.
2. Although an alternating pressure mattress will evenly distribute pressure over bony prominences, it will not prevent external rotation.
3. A footboard will prevent footdrop but will not prevent external rotation.
4. **The use of a trochanter roll will prevent external rotation of limbs.**

Classification

Cognitive Level: Application
Competency Category: Foundations of practice

References

Lewis, S.L., et al. (2010), p. 1756
Potter, P.A., Perry, A.G., Ross-Kerr, J.C., & Wood, M.J. (2009), p. 1212

103. Correct answer: 3

1. Restraints do not prevent falls or injuries. Less restrictive interventions must be tried first.
2. Nocturia has not been identified as a reason for his nighttime ambulation.
3. **Modifications in the health-care facility can reduce the risk of falls.**
4. It is possible that Mr. Olsen will attempt to climb over the bed rails.

Classification

Cognitive Level: Application
Competency Category: Foundations of practice

References

Kozier, B., et al. (2010), p. 775
Potter, P.A., Perry, A.G., Ross-Kerr, J.C., & Wood, M.J. (2010), p. 389

104. Correct answer: 2

1. There is nothing to indicate that blood sugars are a priority.
2. **Assessment including vital signs is the first step in the nursing process.**
3. Assessment should be completed prior to the administration of a p.r.n. medication.
4. He should sit upright in bed, not lie flat.

Classification

Cognitive Level: Critical Thinking
Competency Category:
Foundations of practice

References

Lewis, S.L., et al. (2010), p. 1756
Potter, P.A., Perry, A.G., Ross-Kerr, J.C., & Wood, M.J. (2010), p. 494

105. Correct answer: 4

1. Potassium chloride will not have an effect on respirations.
2. Urinary output should decrease after the diuretic is discontinued.
3. One banana would not significantly impact Mrs. Bourgoin's serum potassium values.
4. **Prescribed IV KCl administration and discontinuation of furosemide will result in elevated serum potassium levels. Immediate nursing action is required for hyperkalemia.**

Classification

Cognitive Level: Critical Thinking
Competency Category:
Foundations of practice

References

CPS (2010), p. 1796
Lehne, R.A. (2010), pp. 446-449

106. Correct answer: 4

1. This response does not address the client's concerns and is false reassurance.
2. Returning to the hospital is not a feasible solution.
3. This response does not address the client's concerns.
4. **A support group could provide him with a social network and assistance on living with a colostomy.**

Classification

Cognitive Level: Application
Competency Category:
Collaborative Practice

References

Lewis, S.L., et al. (2010), p. 1149
Potter, P.A., Perry, A.G., Ross-Kerr, J.C., & Wood, M.J. (2010), p. 488

107. Correct answer: 2

1. Mrs. North should avoid pressure against the popliteal space to prevent clot formation and progression.
2. **With the increased risk of bleeding while on an anticoagulant, using an electric razor would reduce the risk of accidental injury and bleeding.**
3. Thirty seconds is not an adequate amount of time for bleeding to stop.
4. Exercise is contraindicated for clients with a deep vein thrombosis because emboli may occur.

Classification

Cognitive Level: Application
Competency Category:
Foundations of practice

References

Clayton, B.D., Stock, Y.N., & Cooper, S.E. (2010), p. 420
Lewis, S.L., et al. (2010), p. 980

108. Correct answer: 4

1. Practical nurses should not administer medications that they have not prepared themselves.
2. At this point, it is premature to assign blame and to name a colleague who may be responsible.
3. This is not an appropriate nursing action for this situation.
4. **There is no way to verify when the dose was prepared. Nurses should not administer medications that they have not prepared themselves.**

Classification

Cognitive Level: Critical Thinking
Competency Category:
Professional, ethical and legal practice

References

Perry, A.G., & Potter, P.A. (2010), pp. 691-695
Potter, P.A., Perry, A.G., Stockert, P., & Hall, A. (2011), pp. 395-396

109. Correct answer: 2

1. Urinary catheter irrigation is not an intake.
2. **Blood transfusions are considered intake.**
3. Solid foods are not calculated as fluid intake.
4. Nasogastric drainage is recorded as an output.

Classification

Cognitive Level: Knowledge/Comprehension
Competency Category:
Foundations of practice

References

Potter, P.A., Perry, A.G., Ross-Kerr, J.C., & Wood, M.J. (2010), pp. 947-949
Potter, P.A., Perry, A.G., Stockert, P., & Hall, A. (2011), pp. 467-469

110. Correct answer: 2

1. Body image changes affect each client differently. Knowledge level should be assessed first.
2. **Client's present knowledge level should be assessed to identify appropriate teaching and learning strategies.**
3. Teaching resources are individualized. Appropriate teaching tools should be selected following an assessment of her learning needs.
4. Colostomy support groups can be very helpful depending on client's needs and readiness. However, this is not a preoperative strategy.

Classification

Cognitive Level: Application
Competency Category:
Collaborative practice

References

Lewis, S.L., et al. (2010), p. 1147
Perry, A.G., & Potter, P.A. (2010), p. 301

111. Correct answer: 4

1. This does not assess the client's readiness for discharge.
2. This does not assess if the client has understood the discharge information.
3. A return demonstration would better assess the client's knowledge and capability.
4. **An assessment of Mrs. Cormier's ostomy knowledge is the first step in discharge planning.**

Classification

Cognitive Level: Critical Thinking
Competency Category:
Foundations of practice

References

Lewis, S.L., et al. (2010), p. 1149
Perry, A.G., & Potter, P.A. (2010), p. 310

112. Correct answer: 2

1. This does not imply consent to the procedure.
2. **Implied consent exists when the individual's non-verbal behaviour indicates agreement.**
3. This does not imply consent to the procedure. It may imply refusal.
4. This does not imply consent to the procedure.

Classification

Cognitive Level: Application
Competency Category:
Professional, ethical and legal practice

References

Berman, A., Snyder, S.J., Kozier, B., & Erb, G. (2008), pp. 60-61
Potter, P.A., Perry A.G., Ross-Kerr, J.C., & Wood, M.J. (2010), p. 108

113. Correct answer: 2

1. These would require airborne precautions.
2. **These diseases require droplet precautions.**
3. These would require contact precautions.
4. These would require contact precautions.

Classification

Cognitive Level: Application
Competency Category:
Foundations of practice

References

Perry, A.G., & Potter, P.A. (2010), pp. 178-179
Potter, P.A., Perry, A.G., Ross-Kerr, J.C., & Wood, M.J. (2009), p. 657

114. Correct answer: 2

1. A physician's order is required for performing a catheterization.
2. **The bedpan is an option following hip replacement surgery.**
3. Pushing fluids will add to urinary retention.
4. It would be preferable to attempt to use a bedpan first.

Classification

Cognitive Level: Critical Thinking
Competency Category:
Professional, ethical and legal practice

References

Potter, P.A., Perry, A.G., Ross-Kerr, J.C., & Wood, M.J. (2010), p. 1162
Potter, P.A., Perry, A.G., Stockert, P., & Hall, A. (2011), p. 1007

115. Correct answer: 4

1. This does not address the error or safety of the client.
2. This is not the immediate action.
3. This does not address the error or safety of the client.
4. **When a medication error occurs, the client's condition and response need to be assessed. An incident/ occurrence report is required.**

Classification

Cognitive Level: Application
Competency Category:
Professional, ethical and legal practice

References

Perry, A.G., & Potter, P.A. (2010), p. 691
Potter, P.A., Perry, A.G., Stockert, P., & Hall, A. (2011), pp. 395-396

116. Correct answer: 4

1. Jacket restraints should be applied over the client's clothing.
2. Release of side rails while client is being restrained may result in an injury to the client's leg.
3. The restraints should be removed at least every 2 hours.
4. **A quick-release knot allows for quick removal of the restraint in an emergency.**

Classification

Cognitive Level:
Knowledge/Comprehension
Competency Category:
Professional, ethical and legal practice

References

Berman, A., Snyder, S.J., Kozier, B., & Erb, G. (2008), p. 735
Potter, P.A., Perry, A.G., Stockert, P., & Hall, A. (2011), pp. 738-742

117. Correct answer: 2

1. This is not the best practice because orders may have changed.
2. **Appropriate procedure includes checking the physician's order.**
3. It is not necessary to change the IV tubing set with every bag change.
4. It is not necessary to wear gloves when changing the solution container.

Classification

Cognitive Level: Knowledge / Comprehension
Competency Category:
Foundations of practice

References

Perry, A.G., & Potter, P.A. (2010), p. 744
Potter, P.A., Perry, A.G., Stockert, P., & Hall, A. (2011), pp. 513-516

118. Correct answer: 3

1. While the practical nurse would reinforce the teaching of deep breathing, it would be appropriate to find out why he is reluctant.
2. There is no indication at this point that the client's reluctance to deep breathe is related to pain.
3. **It is important to find out why he is reluctant to deep breathe.**
4. This would be important, but the practical nurse should first assess why he is reluctant to deep breathe.

Classification

Cognitive Level: Critical Thinking
Competency Category:
Foundations of practice

References

Perry, A.G., & Potter, P.A. (2010), p. 115
Potter, P.A., Perry, A.G., Stockert, P., & Hall, A. (2011), pp. 200-201

119. Correct answer: 2

1. It is not necessary to use an antiseptic solution.
2. **Warm water will remove any spray that has accumulated around the mouthpiece that could interfere with the proper distribution of spray during use.**
3. It is not necessary to follow sterile procedure.
4. A cloth may not remove dried-on spray.

Classification

Cognitive Level: Application
Competency Category:
Foundations of practice

References

Berman, A., et al. (2008), p. 897
Perry, A.G., & Potter, P.A. (2010), pp. 719-721

120. Correct answer: 2

1. This response does not reflect listening skills.
2. **This strategy reflects empathy and promotes dialogue.**
3. This response does not explore the problem with the client.
4. This is a non-therapeutic communication technique.

Classification

Cognitive Level: Application
Competency Category:
Foundations of practice

References

Potter, P.A., Perry, A.G., Ross-Kerr, J.C., & Wood, M.J. (2009), pp. 394-395
Potter, P.A., Perry, A.G., Stockert, P., & Hall, A. (2011), p. 176

121. Correct answer: 1

1. **Soaking softens the area, making it easier to shave the client.**
2. The skin should be pulled taut for shaving.
3. Short, firm strokes should be used.
4. Shaving should occur in the direction of hair growth.

Classification

Cognitive Level: Application
Competency Category:
Foundations of practice

References

Perry, A.G., & Potter, P.A. (2010), p. 448
Potter, P.A., & Perry, A.G., Stockert, P., & Hall, A. (2011), p. 769

122. Correct answer: 1

1. **It is the practical nurse's responsibility to report suspected child abuse.**
2. This is not an appropriate action.
3. This is not an appropriate action. The practical nurse should report these observations.
4. Developmentally, Brian may not be able to tell the practical nurse about the abuse. This would be more appropriate with an older child.

Classification

Cognitive Level: Application
Competency Category:
Professional, ethical and legal practice

References

Hockenberry, M.J., & Wilson, D. (2011), p. 638
Pillitteri, A. (2010), pp. 1640-1641

123. Correct answer: 2

1. The practical nurse needs to first assess the client's existing knowledge and understanding of the disease.
2. **The practical nurse needs to assess the client's existing knowledge and understanding of the disease prior to selecting an intervention.**
3. The practical nurse needs to first assess the client's existing knowledge and understanding of the disease.
4. Although this may be appropriate at a later time, it would not be the first approach.

Classification

Cognitive Level: Critical Thinking
Competency Category:
Collaborative practice

References

Potter, P.A., Perry, A.G., Stockert, P., & Hall, A. (2011), p. 201
Stanhope, M., & Lancaster, J. (2008), p. 309

124. Correct answer: 4

1. This is not the reason why a client should be in a left lateral position for an enema.
2. This is not the reason why a client should be in a left lateral position for an enema.
3. Lying down makes it easier to retain, rather than expel, the fluid.
4. **This position allows the flow of solution by gravity into the sigmoid colon and rectum.**

Classification

Cognitive Level: Knowledge/Comprehension
Competency Category:
Foundations of practice

References

Perry, A.G., & Potter, P.A. (2010), p. 910
Potter, P.A., Perry, A.G., Stockert, P., & Hall, A. (2011), p. 1015

125. Correct answer: 4

1. This defuses the present situation and enables the practical nurse to observe the immediate situation in terms of unprofessional misconduct. However, the issue may not be dealt with in a long-term manner.
2. This will not stop this behaviour and will leave this client at risk for future inappropriate behaviour from this colleague.
3. This approach is confrontational and will not likely correct the behaviour.
4. **This enables the practical nurse to respond to the present situation. By talking to the colleague, accountability for professional conduct is addressed.**

Classification

Cognitive Level: Application
Competency Category:
Professional, ethical and legal practice

References

Arnold, E.C., & Undeman Boggs, K. (2007), p. 335
Balzer Riley, J. (2008), p. 309

126. Correct answer: 4

1. This is not an appropriate action.
2. This breaks client confidentiality and does not facilitate change.
3. This is not a police incident.
4. **Involving another team member who can investigate further is the best approach.**

Classification

Cognitive Level: Critical Thinking
Competency Category:
Professional, ethical and legal practice

References

Berman, A., Snyder, S.J., Kozier, B., & Erb, G. (2008), p. 422
Potter, P.A., Perry, A.G., Ross-Kerr, J.C., & Wood, M.J. (2009), p. 388

127. Correct answer: 1

1. **It is important to fully understand his wife's concerns first.**
2. The likelihood of adequate intake is lower if meals are not enjoyed.
3. This statement does not help Mrs. Chan. It implies that she is not trying hard enough.
4. This is not an attempt at helping Mrs. Chan and also assigns blame to her.

Classification

Cognitive Level: Application
Competency Category:
Collaborative practice

References

Berman, A., Snyder, S.J., Kozier, B., & Erb, G. (2008), p. 1095
Potter, P.A., Perry, A.G., Ross-Kerr, J.C., & Wood, M.J. (2009), p. 470

128. Correct answer: 2

1. There are no dairy products in this list.
2. **This choice includes all the food groups.**
3. The milk put in tea is not enough to qualify as a serving. This meal may also be high in fat.
4. All the food groups are not represented.

Classification

Cognitive Level: Application
Competency Category:
Foundations of practice

References

Craven, R.F., & Hirnle, C.J. (2009), pp. 952-955
Potter, P.A., Perry, A.G., Ross-Kerr, J.C., & Wood, M.J. (2009), pp. 1048-1051

129. Correct answer: 2

1. Monitoring intake does not promote consumption.
2. **A person will be more likely to drink fluids that he/she likes.**
3. Accessibility does not ensure intake. There is also no selection of fluids to account for client preferences.
4. Recording a list of the client's favourite beverages does not ensure increased intake.

Classification

Cognitive Level: Application
Competency Category:
Foundations of practice

References

Berman, A., Snyder, S.J., Kozier, B., & Erb, G. (2008), pp. 125-126
Craven, R.F., & Hirnle, C.J. (2009), p. 832

130. Correct answer: 4

1. Only health-care providers involved in the client's care can have access to the client's medical record. This is considered a breach in confidentiality.
2. Notifying the supervisor does not prevent the colleague from viewing the chart.
3. This is inappropriate and unprofessional behaviour.
4. **Only health-care providers involved in the client's care can have access to the client's medical record.**

Classification

Cognitive Level: Application
Competency Category:
Professional, ethical and legal practice

References

Burkhardt, M.A., Nathaniel, A., & Walton, N. (2010), pp. 159-161
Potter, P.A., Perry, A.G., Ross-Kerr, J.C., & Wood, M.J. (2009), p. 105

131. Correct answer: 1

1. **The narcotic dosage may be too high if the client becomes excessively drowsy. As a result, the physician should be notified.**
2. This may not be necessary and implies that the client is abusing the narcotics.
3. This blames the client and does not address the cause of the drowsiness.
4. Drowsiness is not indicative of an allergic reaction.

Classification

Cognitive Level: Application
Competency Category:
Foundations of practice

References

Clayton, B.D., Stock, Y.N., & Cooper, S.E. (2010), p. 318
Lewis, S.L., et al. (2010), pp. 209-210

132. Correct answer: 1

1. **A client should be able to choose when to receive help.**
2. This may be appropriate, but does not promote the client's desire for autonomy.
3. There is no indication that Mrs. Abdul is having difficulty chewing foods.
4. There is no indication that Mrs. Abdul is having difficulty chewing foods.

Classification

Cognitive Level: Application
Competency Category:
Foundations of practice

References

Berman, A., Snyder, S.J., Kozier, B., & Erb, G. (2008), p. 474
Edelman, C.L., & Mandle, C.L. (2010), pp. 127-128

133. Correct answer: 2

1. This does not address the urgency of the situation. The client may have pulmonary emboli.
2. **The client has symptoms of pulmonary emboli. This requires prompt intervention from the practical nurse before calling the physician.**
3. This does not address the urgency of the situation. The client may have pulmonary emboli.
4. This does not address the urgency of the situation. The client may have pulmonary emboli.

Classification

Cognitive Level: Critical Thinking
Competency Category:
Foundations of practice

References

Day, R.A., Paul, P., Williams, B., Smeltzer, S.C., & Bare, B. (2007), pp. 552-554
Lewis, S.L., et al. (2010), pp. 986-987

134. Correct answer: 4

1. This does not deal with the cause of his symptoms. He may be experiencing a transfusion reaction.
2. Further assessment is required to determine if he is having a transfusion reaction.
3. Further assessment is required to determine if he is having a transfusion reaction.
4. **A transfusion reaction would be suspected. The practical nurse should stop the blood transfusion and have the physician informed immediately.**

Classification

Cognitive Level: Application
Competency Category:
Foundations of practice

References

Potter, P.A., Perry, A.G., Ross-Kerr, J.C., & Wood, M.J. (2009), p. 982
Potter, P.A., Perry, A.G., Stockert, P., & Hall, A. (2011), p. 495

135. Correct answer: 1

1. **This is the correct procedure for administering eye drops.**
2. Eye drops should not be omitted from right eye. Secretions are present because of an infection that the eye drops are meant to treat.
3. Spreading the eyelids with a gloved hand may be painful for the client. Eye drops should not be administered into the inner canthus.
4. Eye drops should not be administered into the outer canthus.

Classification

Cognitive Level: Application
Competency Category:
Foundations of practice

References

Berman, A., Snyder, S.J., Kozier, B., & Erb, G. (2008), pp. 887-888
Potter, P.A., Perry, A.G., Stockert, P., & Hall, A. (2011), pp. 436-438

136. Correct answer: 3

1. This is an appropriate action for heparin sodium (Hepalean), not warfarin sodium.
2. Nose bleeds are not a frequent side effect of warfarin sodium.
3. **Some green leafy vegetables contain vitamin K. Vitamin K inhibits the action of warfarin sodium.**
4. An increase in regular exercise would be advised to increase venous blood flow.

Classification

Cognitive Level: Critical Thinking
Competency Category:
Collaborative practice

References

Clayton, B.D., Stock, Y.N., & Cooper, S.E. (2010), pp. 430-431
Lewis, S.L., et al. (2010), p. 979

137. Correct answer: 2

1. Assessment is the first priority. The practical nurse should determine if the drainage system is malfunctioning.
2. **An improperly positioned drainage system or any kinks in the tubing that prevent proper drainage will cause discomfort.**
3. Assessment should be done first. Based on the assessment, irrigation may be required later.
4. Discomfort does not necessarily indicate the need for urinalysis. An assessment should be done first.

Classification

Cognitive Level: Critical Thinking
Competency Category:
Foundations of practice

References

Lewis, S.L., et al. (2010), p. 1263
Perry, A.G., & Potter, P.A. (2010), p. 874

138. Correct answer: 4

1. The system should be changed every 5 to 7 days.
2. The pouch will fall and / or pull off the skin barrier if it is not emptied until full.
3. Irrigation, if ordered, should be done once per day. There is no indication that irrigation is ordered.
4. **This assists with odour control and also minimizes the risk of pouch/phalange disconnection.**

Classification

Cognitive Level: Application
Competency Category:
Foundations of practice

References

Lewis, S.L., et al. (2010), pp. 1147-1148
Perry, A.G., & Potter, P.A. (2010), p. 927

139. Correct answer: 3

1. Consent must be obtained first.
2. This must be done immediately prior to procedure, once consent is obtained.
3. **Before any procedure is done, informed consent must be obtained.**
4. Consent must be obtained first. If consent is denied, the supplies would be wasted.

Classification

Cognitive Level: Knowledge / Comprehension
Competency Category:
Professional, ethical and legal practice

References

Potter, P.A., Perry, A.G., Ross-Kerr, J.C., & Wood, M.J. (2010), p. 107
Potter, P.A., Perry, A.G., Stockert, P., & Hall, A. (2011), p. 53

140. Correct answer: 1

1. **These are signs of excess fluid volume and must be addressed immediately. The practical nurse should anticipate reducing or stopping the IV rate.**
2. These are signs of excess fluid volume and must be addressed immediately.
3. These are signs of excess fluid volume and must be addressed immediately.
4. These are signs of excess fluid volume and must be addressed immediately.

Classification

Cognitive Level: Critical Thinking
Competency Category:
Foundations of practice

References

Perry, A.G., & Potter, P.A. (2010), p. 764
Potter, P.A., Perry, A.G., Stockert, P., & Hall, A. (2011), p. 516

141. Correct answer: 2

1. This does not address the client's feelings.
2. **This response is appropriate because respect includes reflecting in order to understand the client's feelings.**
3. This type of unwarranted reassurance disregards the client's feelings.
4. Asking if the client wants a family member called does not deal directly with his feelings.

Classification

Cognitive Level: Critical Thinking
Competency Category:
Collaborative practice

References

Arnold, E.C., & Undeman Boggs, K. (2007), pp. 214-215
Balzer Riley, J. (2008), p. 25

142. Correct answer: 4

1. The physician's order should be verified first prior to initiating any further actions.
2. The physician's order should be verified first prior to initiating any further actions.
3. The physician's order should be verified first prior to initiating any further actions.
4. **This action is required immediately prior to obtaining blood or blood products in order to verify the correct product.**

Classification

Cognitive Level: Application
Competency Category:
Professional, ethical and legal practice

References

Berman, A., Snyder, S.J., Kozier, B., & Erb, G. (2008), p. 1475
Perry, A.G., & Potter, P.A. (2010), p. 791

143. Correct answer: 3

1. The first step should be to stop the flow.
2. The first step should be to stop the flow.
3. **This is the correct first step. The flow should be stopped by clamping the tubing.**
4. It is not necessary to obtain a physician's order if the IV is leaking.

Classification

Cognitive Level: Critical Thinking
Competency Category:
Foundations of practice

References

Berman, A., Snyder, S.J., Kozier, B., & Erb, G. (2008), p. 1470
Potter, P.A., Perry, A.G., Stockert, P., & Hall, A. (2011), p. 492

144. Correct answer: 2

1. The practical nurse is ignoring the couple's feelings and concerns with this response.
2. **This represents a supportive statement because feelings are acknowledged and some private time is made available.**
3. This response does not include private time in case Mr. and Mrs. Barr need it.
4. Providing time to talk with clients is appropriate, but it is far too soon to expect them to be ready to discuss their plans.

Classification

Cognitive Level: Critical Thinking
Competency Category:
Collaborative practice

References

Arnold, E.C., & Undeman Boggs, K. (2007), pp. 200-205
Balzer Riley, J. (2008), p. 119

145. Correct answer: 2

1. It is more important to discuss the incident with the offender before reporting to a supervisor.
2. **It is important to discuss the incident with the offender before taking any other action.**
3. This is not a professional way to handle inappropriate behaviour. There is also no follow-up to the inappropriate action.
4. An apology is not sufficient because the situation has not been dealt with and may reoccur.

Classification

Cognitive Level: Application
Competency Category:
Professional, ethical and legal practice

References

Arnold, E.C., & Undeman Boggs, K. (2007), p. 325
Shives, L.R. (2008), p. 138

146. Correct answer: 3

1. This may not be appropriate or desired by the daughter or the client.
2. This is not an appropriate or optimal plan.
3. **This is an appropriate recommendation for assistance with daily activities.**
4. Limited resources may not permit this.

Classification

Cognitive Level: Critical Thinking
Competency Category:
Foundations of practice

References

Berman, A., Snyder, S.J., Kozier, B., & Erb, G. (2008), p. 126
Potter, P.A., Perry, A.G., Stockert, P., & Hall, A. (2011), pp. 25-26

147. Correct answer: 3

1. This is not indicative of an adverse reaction to IV therapy.
2. Decreased skin turgor would not occur at the IV site.
3. **An increase in skin temperature at the site is a manifestation of inflammation. This is a complication that can result from IV therapy.**
4. Increased perspiration is not indicative of an adverse reaction to IV therapy.

Classification

Cognitive Level: Application
Competency Category:
Foundations of practice

References

Berman, A., Snyder, S.J., Kozier, B., & Erb, G. (2008), pp. 1467-1468
Perry, A.G., & Potter, P.A. (2010), p. 780

148. Correct answer: 2

1. This approach excludes Mr. Desroches from care planning.
2. **It is important to include Mr. Desroches in care planning.**
3. This approach excludes Mr. Desroches from care planning.
4. This approach excludes Mr. Desroches from care planning.

Classification

Cognitive Level: Application
Competency Category:
Foundations of practice

References

Berman, A., Snyder, S.J., Kozier, B., & Erb, G. (2008), p. 217
Lewis S.L., et al. (2010), p. 12

149. Correct answer: 1

1. **Whole blood is commonly used to replace blood lost during a surgery.**
2. Fluid volume is usually maintained by IV fluid during surgery.
3. This is not the purpose of whole blood during a surgery.
4. This is not the purpose of whole blood during a surgery.

Classification

Cognitive Level: Application
Competency Category:
Foundations of practice

References

Berman, A., Snyder, S.J., Kozier, B., & Erb, G. (2008), p. 1473
Potter, P.A., Perry, A.G., Stockert, P., & Hall, A. (2011), p. 492

150. Correct answer: 2

1. Milk is not easily digested by people with diarrhea and vomiting. It could aggravate the condition.
2. **Small amounts of clear fluids are ordered as tolerated when a diet is initiated after gastroenteritis.**
3. Orange juice is not a clear fluid, even if diluted.
4. Cream soup is not a clear fluid.

Classification

Cognitive Level: Application
Competency Category:
Professional, ethical and legal practice

References

Craven, R.F., & Hirnle, C.J. (2009), p. 971
Hockenberry, M.J., & Wilson, D. (2011), p. 1099

151. Correct answer: 4

1. A change in infusion site will not impact the client's respiratory status.
2. A physician's order is typically needed to discontinue the IV.
3. The rate needs to be slowed, not increased.
4. **Slowing the IV rate will decrease circulatory overload while maintaining the IV site.**

Classification

Cognitive Level: Application
Competency Category:
Foundations of practice

References

Berman, A., Snyder, S.J., Kozier, B., & Erb, G. (2008), pp. 1467-1468
Potter, P.A., Perry, A.G., Stockert, P., & Hall, A. (2011), p. 492

152. Correct answer: 3

1. The infusion rate is questionable for this client and the physician's order needs to be verified. The practical nurse should not decrease the infusion rate immediately.
2. The type of solution and the rate of infusion are questionable for this client. The practical nurse must take action.
3. **The rate and type of solution are questionable for this client. The practical nurse's first action is to verify the physician's order.**
4. The appropriate action for the practical nurse is to verify the physician's order.

Classification

Cognitive Level: Critical Thinking
Competency Category:
Professional, ethical and legal practice

References

Berman, A., Snyder, S.J., Kozier, B., & Erb, G. (2008), pp. 1467-1468
Potter, P.A., Perry, A.G., Stockert, P., & Hall, A. (2011), pp. 491-492

153. Correct answer: 1

1. **To ensure proper technique, a return demonstration would be preferable.**
2. Documentation is important but does not evaluate learning.
3. Explanation of the procedure does not evaluate learning. A return demonstration would be preferable.
4. Deep breathing technique should be assessed first.

Classification

Cognitive Level: Critical Thinking
Competency Category:
Foundations of practice

References

Lewis, S.L., et al. (2010), p. 79
Potter, P.A., Perry, A.G., Stockert, P., & Hall, A. (2011), pp. 1146-1147

154. Correct answer: 3

1. Calluses do not need to be reported.
2. This observation may represent a problem, but does not need to be reported immediately.
3. **Hangnails present a risk for infection and should be reported immediately.**
4. This may indicate poor nutrition but does not need to be reported immediately.

Classification

Cognitive Level: Application
Competency Category:
Collaborative practice

References

Lewis, S.L., et al. (2010), pp. 1368-1369
Perry, A.G., & Potter, P.A. (2010), p. 566

155. Correct answer: 4

1. Nutritional supplements would increase caloric intake. Since he is on a restricted calorie diet, this would not be appropriate.
2. This response does not address the client's request.
3. This response does not address the client's request.
4. **A supplement would increase the caloric intake beyond this client's restriction.**

Classification

Cognitive Level: Application
Competency Category:
Foundations of practice

References

Berman, A., Snyder, S.J., Kozier, B., & Erb, G. (2008), pp. 1236-1238
Lewis, S.L., et al. (2010), pp. 1048-1049

156. Correct answer: 2

1. This does not meet the needs of the family in a culturally sensitive way.
2. **Maintaining integrity of rituals and mourning practices helps families accept the death.**
3. This is not respectful of the client's cultural beliefs and does not address the request.
4. This does not address the family's request. It would be inappropriate to ask family members to dress Mr. Marchbank themselves.

Classification

Cognitive Level: Critical Thinking
Competency Category:
Foundations of practice

References

Jarvis, C. (2009), p. 38
Potter, P.A., Perry, A.G., Ross-Kerr, J.C., & Wood, M.J. (2010), pp. 470-472

157. Correct answer: 1

1. **This response is empathetic and indicates that the practical nurse has listened to the client and understands how he feels.**
2. This statement contains more sympathy than empathy. It is therefore sub-optimal.
3. This does not attempt to understand what the client is experiencing and is misleading.
4. This statement discounts the client's desire to see his mother by attempting to distract him.

Classification

Cognitive Level: Critical Thinking
Competency Category:
Collaborative practice

References

Austin, W., & Boyd, M.A. (2010), pp. 128-129
Berman, A., Snyder, S.J., Kozier, B., & Erb, G. (2008), pp. 473-474

158. Correct answer: 4

1. Using a mechanical lift without assistance is not an appropriate action.
2. This action does not maintain client safety or follow the facility's policy.
3. This response does not address the colleague's request.
4. **This response is consistent with the facility's policy and promotes the safety of the client and the employees.**

Classification

Cognitive Level: Critical Thinking
Competency Category:
Professional, ethical and legal practice

References

Berman, A., Snyder, S.J., Kozier, B., & Erb, G. (2008), p. 1146
Potter, P.A., Perry, A.G., Ross-Kerr, J.C., & Wood, M.J. (2010), p. 1221

159. Correct answer: 3

1. Itchy skin is not a complication of diarrhea and vomiting.
2. Reddened skin would only be a local manifestation of a complication of diarrhea.
3. **Poor skin turgor is indicative of dehydration. Dehydration is a complication of diarrhea and vomiting.**
4. This is not a complication of diarrhea and vomiting.

Classification

Cognitive Level: Application
Competency Category:
Foundations of practice

References

Lewis, S.L., et al. (2010), p. 1113
Potter, P.A., Perry, A.G., Ross-Kerr, J.C., & Wood, M.J. (2010), p. 941

160. Correct answer: 3

1. This is not necessary.
2. This is not the first action.
3. **Clients have the right to make informed decisions about their medical care. Explaining the procedure should be done prior to obtaining informed consent.**
4. The client must be made aware of all relevant information related to the procedure before being able to provide consent.

Classification

Cognitive Level: Critical Thinking
Competency Category:
Professional, ethical and legal practice

References

Day, R.A., Paul, P., Williams, B., Smeltzer, S.C., & Bare, B. (2007), p. 407
Potter, P.A., Perry, A.G., Ross-Kerr, J.C., & Wood, M.J. (2010), p. 107

161. Correct answer: 3

1. Organ donation is voluntary, not essential.
2. In cases of suicide, family consent is not usually necessary.
3. **Death from unusual or unknown circumstances requires a coroner's investigation.**
4. There is no indication that the hospital is at fault at this time.

Classification

Cognitive Level: Knowledge/Comprehension
Competency Category:
Professional, ethical and legal practice

References

Berman, A., Snyder, S.J., Kozier, B., & Erb, G. (2008), pp. 64-67
Potter, P.A., Perry, A.G., Stockert, P., & Hall, A. (2011), p. 55

162. Correct answer: 4

1. This does not address the concern. Further assessment is required.
2. This addresses the issue of feeding but not the problem of jaundice.
3. This is not an appropriate action to address the concern.
4. **Physiologic jaundice is treated primarily by phototherapy.**

Classification

Cognitive Level: Critical Thinking
Competency Category:
Foundations of practice

References

Evans, R.J., Evans, M.K., Brown, Y.M.R., & Orshan, S.H. (2010), p. 883
Hockenberry, M.J., & Wilson, D. (2011), pp. 289-292

163. Correct answer: 2

1. This is not the first priority. Maintaining oxygenation is the first priority.
2. **Maintaining oxygenation is the first priority.**
3. This is not the first priority. Maintaining oxygenation is the first priority.
4. This is not the first priority. Maintaining oxygenation is the first priority.

Classification

Cognitive Level: Critical Thinking
Competency Category:
Foundations of practice

References

Berman, A., Snyder, S.J., Kozier, B., & Erb, G. (2008), p. 957
Timby, B.K., & Smith, N.E. (2007), pp. 252-253

164. Correct answer: 3

1. There is no indication that Mr. Azizi cannot make his own decisions. This is therefore not a legally appropriate response.
2. There is no indication that Mr. Azizi cannot make his own decisions. This is therefore not a legally appropriate response.
3. **Mr. Azizi's ability to make his own decisions would need to be assessed. This information would assist the son in becoming a substitute decision-maker if it is deemed necessary.**
4. This is not an appropriate response at this time.

Classification

Cognitive Level: Application
Competency Category:
Professional, ethical and legal practice

References

Berman, A., Snyder, S.J., Kozier, B., & Erb, G. (2008), p. 957
Potter, P.A., Perry, A.G., Ross-Kerr, J.C., & Wood, M.J. (2010), p. 107

165. Correct answer: 2

1. This rate would be too slow. The appropriate drip rate is 50 drops / min.
2. **The correct drop rate is [(50 mL/h) × (60 drops/mL)] ÷ 60 min/h = 50 drops/min.**
3. This rate would be too fast. The appropriate drip rate is 50 drops / min.
4. The present rate of 60 drops / min is too fast. The appropriate drip rate is 50 drops / min.

Classification

Cognitive Level: Application
Competency Category:
Foundations of practice

References

Berman, A., Snyder, S.J., Kozier, B., & Erb, G. (2008), p. 1465
Potter, P.A., Perry, A.G., Ross-Kerr, J.C., & Wood, M.J. (2010), pp. 970-971

166. Correct answer: 2

1. This indicates that he may not be planning to do the injections himself.
2. **This indicates that he is interested and motivated to learn.**
3. This indicates that he is not accepting of his diagnosis and is not ready to learn.
4. This indicates that the client may be anxious about the insulin injections.

Classification

Cognitive Level: Critical Thinking
Competency Category:
Foundations of practice

References

Clayton, B. D., Stock, Y.N., & Cooper, S.E. (2010), pp. 54-55
Potter, P.A., Perry, A.G., Ross-Kerr, J.C., & Wood, M.J. (2009), pp. 300-304

167. Correct answer: 1

1. **This is the proper technique to keep the artificial eye clean and to prevent infection.**
2. Antiseptic solution would cause irritation to the lacrimal ducts.
3. Wiping from the outer to inner canthus would increase the chance of pushing debris into the ducts and the unaffected eye.
4. An antiseptic solution would cause irritation to the lacrimal ducts.

Classification

Cognitive Level: Knowledge / Comprehension
Competency Category:
Foundations of practice

References

Berman, A., Snyder, S.J., Kozier, B., & Erb, G. (2008), p. 782
Potter, P.A., Perry, A.G., Ross-Kerr, J.C., & Wood, M.J. (2010), pp. 866-867

168. Correct answer: 2

1. This does not address the issue. From a professional and legal perspective, this incident must be reported.
2. **From a professional and legal perspective, this incident must be reported.**
3. The occurrence should be reported to a supervisor immediately. Documentation can occur later.
4. The occurrence should be reported to a supervisor immediately. A narcotics count can be conducted later if necessary.

Classification

Cognitive Level: Application
Competency Category:
Professional, ethical and legal practice

References

Burkhardt, N.A., Nathaniel, A., & Walton, N. (2010), p. 202
Marquis, B.L., & Huston, C.J. (2009), pp. 92-97

169. Correct answer: 1

1. **IV infusions may be easily occluded by kinked tubing. This would decrease flow rate.**
2. A decreasing level of fluid in the container may decrease the flow rate.
3. Eye-level height is determined by the height of the observer. If the observer is short, the container at eye level may not be at least 1 metre above the height of the infusion site.
4. The fluid level in the drip chamber does not affect flow rate.

Classification

Cognitive Level: Application
Competency Category:
Foundations of practice

References

Berman, A., Snyder, S.J., Kozier, B., & Erb, G. (2008), p. 1467
Potter, P.A., Perry, A.G., Stockert, P., & Hall, A. (2011), p. 758

170. Correct answer: 3

1. Inflammation around the IV site indicates an infection, not infiltration.
2. Coolness around the IV site is not an indication of inflammation.
3. **For fluid to infuse at the proper rate, the IV tubing must be free of obstruction.**
4. This is not relevant.

Classification

Cognitive Level: Critical Thinking
Competency Category:
Foundations of practice

References

Berman, A., Snyder, S.J., Kozier, B., & Erb, G. (2008), p. 1467
Potter, P.A., Perry, A.G., Stockert, P., & Hall, A. (2011), p. 758

171. Correct answer: 4

1. Anti-embolytic stockings would require an order. Even if they were ordered, they should have been applied prior to ambulation.
2. This would not help the client; it would be painful and could lead to skin breakdown.
3. Heat increases oxygen demands and blood flow demands of the tissue.
4. **Elevating Mr. Albert's legs increases venous return by gravity.**

Classification

Cognitive Level: Application
Competency Category:
Foundations of practice

References

Day, R.A., Paul, P., Williams, B., Smeltzer, S.C., & Bare, B. (2007), p. 837
Lewis, S.L., et al. (2010), p. 978

172. Correct answer: 3

1. This does not address the seriousness of the situation. Coffee-ground material indicates bleeding.
2. There is no indication that this is necessary because the nasogastric tube is draining liquid.
3. **Coffee-ground material indicates bleeding. As a result, the physician should be notified.**
4. This can only be done following a physician's order.

Classification

Cognitive Level: Application
Competency Category:
Foundations of practice

References

Day, R.A., Paul, P., Williams, B., Smeltzer, S.C., & Bare, B. (2007), p. 1023
Lewis, S.L., et al. (2010), p. 1081

173. Correct answer: 4

1. This crosses the line between the therapeutic nurse-client relationship.
2. This is not an appropriate action.
3. This crosses the line between the therapeutic nurse-client relationship.
4. **The practical nurse should recognize Mrs. Summer's need for social interaction.**

Classification

Cognitive Level: Critical Thinking
Competency Category:
Professional, ethical and legal practice

References

Arnold, E.C., & Undeman Boggs, K. (2007), p. 129
Craven, R.F., & Hirnle, C.J. (2009), pp. 329-330

174. Correct answer: 1

1. **Pain is the first priority. In some facilities, pain is considered the fifth vital sign.**
2. Offering fluids should not be the first priority.
3. A scheduled dressing change should not be the first priority.
4. Providing assistance to the bathroom should not be the first priority.

Classification

Cognitive Level: Critical Thinking
Competency Category:
Foundations of practice

References

Day, R.A., Paul, P., Williams, B., Smeltzer, S.C., & Bare, B. (2007), pp. 223-224
Potter, P.A., Perry, A.G., Ross-Kerr, J.C., & Wood, M.J. (2010), pp. 1018-1019, 1031

175. Correct answer: 3

1. Careful handwashing before and after dressing change is adequate protection unless blood and body fluid precautions are necessary.
2. Mask and sterile gloves are not necessary for simple dressing change.
3. **Careful handwashing before and after dressing change is essential for good medical asepsis.**
4. Hydrogen peroxide should not be used to cleanse the ulcerated skin. Normal saline should be used.

Classification

Cognitive Level: Application
Competency Category:
Foundations of practice

References

Craven, R.F., & Hirnle, C.J. (2009), p. 470
Potter, P.A., Perry, A.G., Ross-Kerr, J.C., & Wood, M.J. (2010), p. 649

176. Correct answer: 3

1. This would indicate poor prioritization.
2. Although keeping the team leader informed is important, the practical nurse is responsible for prioritizing client care.
3. **Part of organizing multiple needs is to anticipate potential disruptions to the plan.**
4. This is not a flexible approach.

Classification

Cognitive Level: Critical Thinking
Competency Category:
Foundations of practice

References

Kozier, B., et al. (2010), pp. 445, 451
Potter, P.A., Perry, A.G., Ross-Kerr, J.C., & Wood, M.J. (2010), pp. 179-180

177. Correct answer: 1

1. **The practical nurse should assess his current level of knowledge first and then answer his questions.**
2. This approach could mean that the husband's questions will not get answered.
3. This passes the responsibility to someone else. The practical nurse should attempt to answer his questions first.
4. This approach assumes that the husband's questions are specifically about palliative care. The practical nurse should first determine the nature of his questions.

Classification

Cognitive Level: Critical Thinking
Competency Category:
Collaborative practice

References

Craven, R.F., & Hirnle, C.J. (2009), p. 348
Kozier, B., et al. (2010), p. 520

178. Correct answer: 2

1. Constant observation is only necessary when a client's life is in immediate danger (e.g., suicide); this would not necessarily meet a client's general need for psychological safety.
2. **By increasing her familiarity with the environment, the practical nurse would make her feel more secure, therefore more psychologically safe.**
3. A pleasant view may promote psychological comfort but does not necessarily promote safety.
4. Non-slip rugs help to ensure the client's physical safety rather than psychological safety.

Classification

Cognitive Level: Application
Competency Category:
Foundations of practice

References

Ignatavicius, D.D., & Workman, M.L. (2010), p. 18
Kozier, B., et al. (2010), p. 356

179. Correct answer: 3

1. Peter should not reduce or discontinue taking insulin.
2. Desserts are not the only foods he needs to discontinue.
3. **This is the best response. Peter is aware of the importance of glucose monitoring, insulin administration and diet control.**
4. Peter needs to monitor his glucose levels to maintain a normal range.

Classification

Cognitive Level: Critical Thinking
Competency Category:
Foundations of practice

References

Kozier, B., et al. (2010), p. 532
Potter, P.A., Perry, A.G., Ross-Kerr, J.C., & Wood, M.J. (2010), p. 309

180. Correct answer: 1

1. **Stopping the transfusion should be the first step. It is also important to keep the vein open, and then obtain vital signs and have the physician notified.**
2. The first action should be to stop the blood transfusion.
3. The first action should be to stop the blood transfusion.
4. The first action should be to stop the blood transfusion.

Classification

Cognitive Level: Critical Thinking
Competency Category:
Foundations of practice

References

Kozier, B., et al. (2010), p. 1420
Potter, P.A., Perry, A.G., Ross-Kerr, J.C., & Wood, M.J. (2010), pp. 979-982

8

CPNRE Predictor Test

8

CPNRE Predictor Test

The CPNRE Predictor Test is a tool designed to help you gauge how ready you are to take the CPNRE and to help focus your studying by identifying areas in which you are weak. It provides you with the following:

- Your score on the Predictor Test;
- Your probability of passing the CPNRE;
- Your scoring profile which displays your score in each of the competency categories tested by the CPNRE. This allows you to determine in which areas you need to focus your studying;
- The ability to review the questions and correct answers for a 24-hour period.

The Predictor Test is a short version of the national exam. It is created using the same methods as the CPNRE and the questions in the Predictor Test have all been used on previous administrations of the CPNRE. The Predictor Test is updated every time the Blueprint of the exam is updated.

Format of the Test

There are two Predictor Tests available for purchase. Each Predictor Test has 100 multiple-choice questions matching the Blueprint for the CPNRE.

- Predictor Test 1 and Predictor Test 2 have completely different sets of questions, but are similar in difficulty.
- Both tests contain case-based and independent questions.
- Each test comes in both French and English, and you can switch freely between languages while taking the test.
- The test comes equipped with a timer to simulate an actual exam environment.
- If, for some reason, you have to stop the test before completing it, you will be able to return to the test later provided you have not yet submitted your answers.
- Once you have completed the test and submitted your answers, you will be presented with your results and the option to print them. Your results will also be e-mailed to the e-mail address you provided when you purchased the test.
- You will also have the opportunity to log back in to your test within 24 hours to view the questions and correct answers again. After the 24-hour period, you will no longer have access to this information.

How to use the Predictor Test

The Predictor Test is designed to help gauge your readiness to write the CPNRE and to help focus your studying by identifying areas of weakness. The Predictor Test is most useful when taken under test-like conditions. You should adhere to the time limit of 2.5 hours and not use any notes or textbooks when taking the test. The prediction of readiness to take the CPNRE will only be meaningful and useful if you follow these instructions and complete the Predictor Test without any assistance.

Depending on your situation, the two tests can be used together or separately. When taken at the same time, greater precision in gauging your readiness to write the CPNRE is achieved. This may be most informative for candidates who have only a short period of time before the CPNRE administration date. In contrast, when the two tests are taken separately, the results of the first test can be used to develop a more focused program of study. After studying for some time, the second Predictor Test could then be completed to re-assess your readiness to write the exam and provide additional focus for studying prior to your exam date.

Test Scoring

Your total score on the Predictor Test is calculated as the number of questions on the test that you answered correctly. In addition to your total test score, your performance is also presented by cognitive level and competency framework level. Your performance on each level is calculated as the number of questions in that level that you answered correctly.

By comparing your performance on the questions in the Predictor Test to the performance of thousands of candidates who have written previous administrations of the actual CPNRE, we are able to estimate what your score would be on the CPNRE. From this estimated score, we can calculate your probability of passing the CPNRE.

Once you have completed the Predictor Test and submitted your answers, you will be presented with your score on the Predictor Test, your probability of passing the CPNRE and a scoring profile showing your score in each of the competency categories tested by the CPNRE.

Test Results

A sample results profile is presented next.

Canadian Practical Nurse Registration Predictor Test

Your Results Profile!

Your score on the Predictor Test is converted to a common measurement scale and compared against the established passing point used for the CPNRE. Based on your performance on the Predictor Test, the probability of passing the Canadian Practical Nurse Registration Examination was calculated and found to be 95% - 100%, as shown in the graph below.

Probability of Passing the Canadian Practical Nurse Registration Examination

<20%	20%-25%	25%-30%	30%-35%	35%-40%	40%-45%	45%-50%	50%-55%	55%-60%	60%-65%	65%-70%	70%-75%	75%-80%	80%-85%	85%-90%	90%-95%	>95%
																95%-100%

Your performance on the Predictor Test demonstrates how equipped you are to take the CPNRE. Continue with your exam preparation to maintain your level of readiness. Be sure to review your Performance Profile to gain a better understanding of your areas of weakness in the competency categories.

Cognitive Levels	Your Score	Perfect Score
Knowledge/Comprehension	23	26
Application	52	55
Critical Thinking	18	19
	93	100

Competency Category	Your Score	Perfect Score
Professional, Ethical and Legal Practice	17	19
Foundations of Practice	58	61
Collaborative Practice	18	20
	93	100

Technical Requirements

The Predictor Test is only available as an online test. In order to take the test, you will require the following:

1. A computer connected to the Internet.
2. Microsoft Internet Explorer version 5.5 or higher, Netscape version 6.0 or higher or Firefox 1.0 or higher.

How do I Purchase the Test?

The Predictor Tests can only be purchased online using Visa or MasterCard. We provide a secure Internet credit card transaction to ensure that your personal credit card information is protected. Our web site does not support debit card payments. The tests can only be taken online. They are not available in hard copy or on CD. Once you have taken the Predictor Test, you will not be able to re-take the test unless you purchase it again.

The suggested retail price for one test is $39.95 (plus tax) and for two tests is $63.90 (plus tax). **Prices are subject to change, see www.CPNRE.ca**. If you purchase both tests at the same time, you will save 40% off the price of the second test. If you purchase the second test later, you will not receive this discount.

After you have completed the purchase, you will receive a username and password and you will be sent to a Login page. You can take the test right away by logging in using your username and password or you can take the test later.

Frequently Asked Questions

What is the difference between the CPNRE Predictor Test and the CPNRE Prep Guide?

The *CPNRE Prep Guide* is designed to help you review and integrate the concepts you have learned in your practical nursing program; it will also help you assess your skills in applying that knowledge. The prep guide can be used to enhance your readiness to write the CPNRE. In comparison, the Predictor Test is designed to help you gauge your readiness for the CPNRE. By using the *CPNRE Prep Guide* and conducting an analysis of your performance on the CPNRE Predictor Test, you will be able to identify your strengths and weaknesses and develop a more focused study program.

What is the difference between the CPNRE Predictor Test and the Practice Exam in the CPNRE Prep Guide?

The Practice Exam found in the *CPNRE Prep Guide* is a 180-question sample test that is built according to the *CPNRE Blueprint*. The primary purpose of this sample test is to help the candidate prepare to write the CPNRE. Candidates are provided with a full sample test along with an answer key, rationales and two current references. Candidates can also create a performance profile to identify areas of strength and weakness. As such, it is an excellent study tool. The prep guide Practice Exam is available in a paper-based format and on CD-ROM.

The CPNRE Predictor Test is a 100-question sample test that is also built according to the *CPNRE Blueprint*. However, the primary purpose of this test is to gauge a candidate's readiness to write the CPNRE; it is not primarily a study tool. At the completion of the Predictor Test, candidates are provided with a performance profile and a probability of passing the CPNRE. For a 24-hour period, candidates can also return to their completed Predictor Test to see which questions they answered correctly and incorrectly; however, they are not provided with rationales or references. The CPNRE Predictor Test is available exclusively online. It is not available in a paper-based format or on CD-ROM.

If I buy both Predictor Tests, what is the best way to use them?

Depending on your situation, the two Predictor Tests can be used either together or separately. When taken at the same time, greater precision in gauging your readiness to write the CPNRE can be achieved. This may be most informative for candidates who have only a short period of time before the CPNRE administration date. In contrast, when the two tests are taken separately, the results of the first test can be used to develop a more focused program of study. After studying for some time, the second Predictor Test could then be completed to re-assess your readiness to write the exam and provide additional focus before the CPNRE administration.

Are the questions in the Predictor Test 1 and 2 different?

Predictor Test 1 and Predictor Test 2 have completely different sets of questions, but are similar in difficulty. Both tests contain case-based and independent multiple-choice questions. Each Predictor Test has 100 multiple-choice questions matching the Blueprint for the Canadian Practical Nurse Registration Examination.

How is my score on the Predictor Test calculated?

Your total score on the Predictor Test is calculated as the number of questions on the test that you answered correctly. In addition to your total test score, your performance is also presented by cognitive level and competency framework level. Your performance on each level is calculated as the number of questions in that level that you answered correctly.

How is my probability of passing the CPNRE calculated?

By comparing your performance on the questions in the Predictor Test to the performance of thousands of candidates who have written previous administrations of the actual CPNRE, we are able to estimate what your score would be on the CPNRE. From this estimated score, we can calculate your probability of passing the CPNRE.

Can I review the questions after I have submitted my answers?

Once you have completed the Predictor Test and submitted your answers, you will be presented with a summary of your performance that includes your score on the Predictor Test, your probability of passing the CPNRE and a scoring profile showing your score in each of the competency categories tested by the CPNRE. At this time, you can review the questions and the correct answers. For up to 24 hours after completing the Predictor Test, you will be able to log back into your test using your assigned username and password to review the questions and answers. After the 24-hour period is up, you will no longer have access to this information.

How many times can I take the Predictor Test?

The Predictor Test can only be taken once. If you would like to take the test again, you will have to purchase the test again. It is less expensive to purchase both Predictor Test 1 and Predictor Test 2 at the same time than to purchase them at different times.

Can I get a printed copy of the Predictor Test?

A printed copy of the Predictor Test is not available. It is also not available on CD-ROM. The test can only be taken on-line.

Does my test have an expiry date?

Once you have purchased a Predictor Test, there is no time limit for taking the test. It can be taken at any time, even months after your purchase.

Is the Predictor Test kept up-to-date with the CPNRE?

The Predictor Test is developed to conform to the Blueprint of the CPNRE. Every time the exam Blueprint is updated, the Predictor Test is updated.

How much is the Predictor Test?

The suggested retail price for one test is $39.95 (plus tax) and for two tests is $63.90 (plus tax). **Prices are subject to change, see www.CPNRE.ca**. If you purchase both tests at the same time, you will save 40% off the price of the second test. If you purchase the second test later, you will not receive this discount.

How do I purchase the test?

You may pay for the test(s) by Visa or MasterCard. We provide a secure Internet credit card transaction to ensure that your personal credit card information is protected. Our web site does not support debit card payments.

After you have completed the purchase, you will receive a username and password which you will need to login to your test. Write this information down. Then you will be sent to a Login page. You can take the test right away by logging in using your username and password or you can take the test later.

Could I try a sample on-line test?

A 10-question sample on-line test is available for you to try to ensure that you are comfortable taking an on-line test prior to purchasing your Predictor Test. You will receive a scoring report at the end of the sample test. Please note that this report is for the sample test only. Examples of the scoring report that you will receive after completing the Predictor Test can be found under Test Results.

What is the time limit for the Predictor Test?

The time limit for the Predictor Test is 2.5 hours (150 minutes). The test comes equipped with a timer to simulate an actual exam environment.

The Predictor Test is most useful when taken under test-like conditions. You should adhere to the time limit of 2.5 hours and not use any notes or textbooks when taking the test. The prediction of readiness to take the CPNRE will only be meaningful and useful if you follow these instructions and complete the Predictor Test without any assistance.

Bibliography

Note: All references are important but bolded references were chosen by the Prep Guide Committee as "key references" for candidates preparing for the Canadian Practical Nurse Registration Examination.

Arnold, E.C., & Undeman Boggs, K. (2007). *Interpersonal relationships: Professional communication skills for nurses* (5th ed.). Philadelphia: Saunders Elsevier.

Austin, W., & Boyd, M.A. (2010). *Psychiatric & mental health nursing for Canadian practice* (2nd ed.). Philadelphia: Lippincott Williams & Wilkins.

Ball, W., Bindler, J., & Cowen, K. (2010). *Child health nursing: Partnering with children and families* (2nd ed.). Upper Saddle River, NJ: Pearson.

Balzer Riley, J. (2008). *Communication in nursing* (6th ed.). St. Louis, MO: Mosby Elsevier.

Berman, A., Snyder, S.J., Kozier, B. & Erb, G. (2008). *Kozier & Erb's fundamentals of nursing: Concepts, process, and practice* (8th ed.). Upper Saddle River, NJ: Pearson Prentice Hall.

Burkhardt, M.A., Nathaniel, A., & Walton, N. (2010). *Ethics and issues in contemporary nursing* (1st ed.). Toronto, ON: Nelson Education.

Canadian Pharmacists Association. (2010). *Compendium of pharmaceuticals and specialties: The Canadian drug reference for health professionals*. Ottawa: Author.

Clayton, B.D., Stock, Y.N., & Cooper, S.E. (2010). *Basic pharmacology for nurses* (15th ed.). St. Louis, MO: Mosby, Elsevier.

Craven, R.F., & Hirnle, C.J. (2009). *Fundamentals of nursing: Health human and function* (6th ed.). Philadelphia: Lippincott Williams & Wilkins.

Day, R.A., Paul, P., Williams, B., Smeltzer, S.C., & Bare, B. (2007). *Brunner & Suddarth's textbook of medical-surgical nursing* (1st Canadian ed.). Philadelphia: Lippincott Williams & Wilkins.

Edelman, C.L., & Mandle, C.L. (2010). *Health promotion throughout the life span* (7th ed.). St. Louis, MO: Elsevier.

Evans, R.J., Evans, M.K., Brown, Y.M.R., & Orshan, S.H. (2010). *Canadian maternity, newborn and women's health nursing* (1st Canadian ed.). Philadelphia: Lippincott Williams & Wilkins.

Harkreader, H., & Hogan, M.A. (2004). *Fundamentals of nursing: Caring & clinical judgment* (2nd ed.). St. Louis, MO: Elsevier Science.

Hockenberry, M.J., & Wilson, D. (2011). *Wong's nursing care of infants and children* (9th ed.). St. Louis, MO: Elsevier, Mosby.

Ignatavicius, D.D., & Workman, M.L. (2010). *Medical-surgical nursing: Patient-centered collaborative care* (6th ed.). St. Louis, MO: Saunders, Elsevier.

Jarvis, C. (2009). *Physical examination & health assessment* (1st Canadian ed.). Toronto, ON: Saunders Elsevier.

Kozier, B., Erb, G., Berman, A., Snyder, S.J., Bouchal, D.S., Hirst, S., Yiu, L., Stamler, L.L., & Buck, M. (2010). *Fundamentals of Canadian nursing: Concepts, process, and practice* (2nd ed.). Toronto, ON: Pearson Canada.

Lehne, R.A. (2010). *Pharmacology for nursing care* (7th ed.). St. Louis, MO: Mosby, Elsevier.

Lewis, S.L., Heitkemper, M.M., Dirksen, S.R., Barry, M.A., Goldsworthy, S., & Goodridge, D. (2010). *Medical-surgical nursing in Canada: Assessment and management of clinical problems* (2nd ed.). St. Louis, MO: Mosby, Elsevier.

Lowdermilk, D., Perry, S.E., & Cashion, M.C. (2011). *Maternity nursing* (8th ed.). Toronto, ON: Mosby Elsevier.

Marquis, B.L., & Huston, C.J. (2009). *Leadership roles and management functions in nursing: Theory and application* (6th ed.). Philadelphia: Lippincott Williams & Wilkins.

Perry, S., Hockenberry, M., Lowdermilk, D., & Wilson, D. (2010). Maternal child nursing care (4th ed.). Maryland Heights, MO: Mosby, Elsevier.

Perry, A.G., & Potter, P.A. (2010). *Clinical nursing skills and techniques* (7th ed.). St. Louis, MO: Mosby, Elsevier.

Pillitteri, A. (2010). *Maternal & child health nursing: Care of the childbearing & childrearing family* (6th ed.). Philadelphia: Lippincott Williams & Wilkins.

Potter, P.A., Perry, A.G., Ross-Kerr, J.C., & Wood, M.J. (2009). *Canadian fundamentals of nursing* (4th ed.). St. Louis, MO: Mosby, Elsevier.

Potter, P.A., Perry, A.G., Ross-Kerr, J.C., & Wood, M.J. (2010). *Canadian fundamentals of nursing* (Rev. 4th ed.). St. Louis, MO: Mosby, Elsevier.

Potter, P.A., Perry, A.G., Stockert, P., & Hall, A. (2011). *Basic nursing* (7th ed.). St. Louis, MO: Mosby, Elsevier.

Rosdahl, C.B., & Kowalski, M.T. (2008). *Textbook of basic nursing* (9th ed.). Philadelphia: Lippincott Williams & Wilkins.

Shives, L.R. (2008). *Psychiatric-mental health nursing* (7th ed.). Philadelphia: Lippincott Williams & Wilkins.

Stanhope, M., & Lancaster, J. (2008). *Community health nursing in Canada*. St. Louis, MO: Mosby, Elsevier.

Taylor, C.R., Lillis, C., Lemone, P., & Lynn, P. (2008). *Fundamentals of nursing: The art and science of nursing care* (6th ed.). Philadelphia: Lippincott Williams & Wilkins.

Timby, B.K., & Smith, N.E. (2007). *Introductory medical-surgical nursing* (9th ed.). Philadelphia: Lippincott Williams & Wilkins.

Townsend, M.C. (2009). *Psychiatric mental health nursing: Concepts of care in evidence-based practice* (6th ed.). Philadelphia: F.A. Davis Company.

Appendix A

The CPNRE list of Competencies

Assumptions

In developing the competencies for the Canadian Practical Nurse Registration Examination (CPNRE), the following assumptions were made.

1. The competencies represent the combined nursing knowledge, skills, behaviours, attitudes, critical thinking and clinical judgments required by entry-level practical nurses across Canada.

2. The foundation of practical nursing is defined by legislation, regulation, scope of practice, standards of practice, code of ethics and entry-level competencies.

3. Practical nurses are responsible and accountable for their decisions and actions.

4. Practical nurses provide, facilitate and promote safe, competent and ethical care.

5. Practical nurses demonstrate leadership in all aspects of practice.

6. Practical nurses deliver care while respecting diversity.

7. Practical nurses care for clients throughout the lifespan.

8. Practical nurses follow a systematic approach when applying the nursing process.

9. Educational programs prepare practical nurses to practise in a variety of settings where health care is promoted and delivered.

10. Practical nurses practise collaboratively, while respecting the shared and unique competencies of other members of the health-care team.

11. Practical nurses advocate for and facilitate change reflecting evidence-informed practice.

12. Practical nurses are knowledgeable about trends and issues that impact the client and the health-care team.

13. Practical nurses are active participants in health promotion, illness prevention, reduction of harm and risk management activities.

14. Practical nurses engage in continuous learning to maintain and enhance competence.

Professional

Competent entry-level practical nurses:		*Importance*
PR-1 are responsible and accountable for their own decisions and actions.		
a. recognize and practise autonomously within scope of practice.	PR-1a	Very important
b. recognize when to seek assistance and guidance.	PR-1b	Very important
c. provide care using critical thinking and clinical judgment for decision-making.	PR-1c	Very important
PR-2 develop the therapeutic nurse-client relationship.		
a. initiate, maintain and terminate the therapeutic nurse-client relationship.	PR-2a	Important
b. provide client care in a non-judgmental manner.	PR-2b	Very important
c. respect clients' right to self-determination, informed decision-making and directives.	PR-2c	Very important
PR-3 demonstrate leadership in all aspects of practice.		
a. assess and develop professional competence.	PR-3a	Very important
b. participate in evidence-informed practice.	PR-3b	Important
c. advocate for clients, self and others.	PR-3c	Important
PR-4 demonstrate professional conduct.		
a. adhere to standards of practice of the profession.	PR-4a	Very important
b. identify and respond to inappropriate behaviour.	PR-4b	Very important
c. identify and respond to incidents of unsafe practice.	PR-4c	Very important
d. identify and respond to incidents of professional misconduct.	PR-4d	Very important

Ethical

Competent entry-level practical nurses:		*Importance*
PR-5 apply the ethical framework of the therapeutic nurse-client relationship.		
a. establish and maintain respect, empathy, trust and integrity in interactions with clients.	PR-5a	Very important
b. recognize and respect the values, opinions, needs and beliefs of clients and self.	PR-5b	Very important
c. respect the obligation of the duty to provide care.	PR-5c	Very important
PR-6 promote clients' rights and responsibilities.		
a. ensure implied and / or informed consent.	PR-6a	Very important
b. protect clients' rights by maintaining confidentiality, privacy and dignity.	PR-6b	Very important
c. support clients' right to self-determination as part of the plan of care.	PR-6c	Important

Legal

Competent entry-level practical nurses:		*Importance*
PR-7 adhere to legal requirements of practice.		
a. adhere to relevant legislation related to abuse, communicable diseases and mental health issues.	PR-7a	Very important
b. recognize and respond to questionable orders, actions or decisions.	PR-7b	Very important
c. practise within established policies, procedures and standards.	PR-7c	Important
PR-8 disclose relevant information to appropriate individuals.		
a. maintain client confidentiality in written, oral and / or electronic communication.	PR-8a	Very important
b. recognize and respond to the clients' right to health-care information.	PR-8b	Important
PR-9 adhere to legal requirements regarding documentation.		
a. document within established policies, procedures and standards.	PR-9a	Very important
b. initiate, receive, transcribe and verify orders.	PR-9b	Very important
c. complete occurrence reports as required.	PR-9c	Important

Assessment

Competent entry-level practical nurses: *Importance*

FP-1 complete comprehensive health assessments of clients throughout the lifespan.

a.	perform individualized health assessments.	FP-1a	Very important
b.	select and utilize appropriate technology.	FP-1b	Important
c.	accommodate individual client diversity.	FP-1c	Important
d.	perform physical assessments, including observation, inspection, auscultation and palpation.	FP-1d	Very important
e.	perform mental, spiritual, emotional, psychological and social assessments.	FP-1e	Important
f.	research relevant clinical data.	FP-1f	Important
g.	interpret and integrate findings from health assessments.	FP-1g	Important

Planning and Implementation

Competent entry-level practical nurses: *Importance*

FP-2 formulate clinical decisions that are consistent with client needs and priorities.

a.	apply critical thinking to respond to changing situations.	FP-2a	Very important
b.	develop individualized nursing interventions.	FP-2b	Important

FP-3 implement nursing interventions based on health assessments and desired outcomes.

a.	identify the nursing diagnoses.	FP-3a	Important
b.	implement the plan of care.	FP-3b	Very important
c.	implement strategies to enhance communicable disease control.	FP-3c	Very important
d.	apply knowledge of immunization principles and implications to the client.	FP-3d	Important

FP-4 utilize effective time management to organize nursing care.

a.	organize multiple demands into manageable interventions.	FP-4a	Important
b.	set priorities that reflect individual client needs.	FP-4b	Very important

FP-5 promote client self-care and wellness.

a.	assist clients to identify actual and potential health goals and outcomes.	FP-5a	Important
b.	support clients to assume responsibility for their health.	FP-5b	Important
c.	involve clients in developing and prioritizing their plan of care.	FP-5c	Important
d.	provide information and access to resources.	FP-5d	Important

FP-6	**facilitate health education.**		
	a. collaborate with clients in the discharge planning process.	FP-6a	Important
	b. plan and implement strategies to enhance client learning.	FP-6b	Important
	c. evaluate client learning and revise strategies as necessary.	FP-6c	Important
FP-7	**apply principles of safety.**		
	a. implement routine practices (standard precautions).	FP-7a	Very important
	b. maintain and promote a safe work environment.	FP-7b	Important
	c. apply principles of infection prevention control.	FP-7c	Very important
	d. implement strategies related to risk management and reduction of harm.	FP-7d	Very important
FP-8	**apply the principles of pharmacology.**		
	a. utilize critical thinking in the application of pharmacological principles.	FP-8a	Very important
	b. assess and review clinical data.	FP-8b	Very important
	c. apply the principles of medication administration.	FP-8c	Very important
	d. implement strategies to enhance and promote medication safety.	FP-8d	Very important
	e. prepare and administer enteral, percutaneous and parenteral (subcutaneous, intramuscular, intradermal and intravenous) medications (excluding IV push).	FP-8e	Very important
	f. assess and document client response to medication.	FP-8f	Very important
FP-9	**apply the principles of infusion therapy.**		
	a. apply knowledge of infusion therapy.	FP-9a	Very important
	b. initiate, assess, monitor and manage hypodermoclysis (HDC).	FP-9b	Important
	c. initiate, assess, monitor and manage peripheral infusion therapy (IV).	FP-9c	Very important
	d. assess and monitor the client with a central venous catheter (CVC).	FP-9d	Very important
	e. assess and document client response to infusion therapy.	FP-9e	Very important
FP-10	**apply the principles of infusion therapy to blood and blood products.**		
	a. apply standards for the safe administration of blood and blood products.	FP-10a	Very important
	b. initiate, assess, monitor and manage infusion of blood and blood products.	FP-10b	Very important
	c. evaluate and document client response to infusion of blood and blood products.	FP-10c	Very important

Evaluation

Competent entry-level practical nurses: *Importance*

FP-11	**perform ongoing evaluation throughout delivery of care.**		
a.	evaluate the effectiveness of nursing interventions.	FP-11a	Very important
b.	compare actual outcomes to expected outcomes.	FP-11b	Important
c.	review and revise the plan of care.	FP-11c	Important

Collaborative Practice

Competent entry-level practical nurses: *Importance*

CP-1	**develop and maintain collaborative relationships with clients and others.**		
a.	initiate and maintain a therapeutic environment.	CP-1a	Important
b.	promote safety, comfort and cultural sensitivity.	CP-1b	Important
c.	encourage and support clients' active participation in care.	CP-1c	Important
CP-2	**communicate collaboratively with the client.**		
a.	gather and/or provide relevant information.	CP-2a	Important
b.	encourage and support the opportunity for client feedback.	CP-2b	Important
c.	utilize communication techniques to provide effective interpersonal interaction.	CP-2c	Very important
d.	apply conflict resolution skills.	CP-2d	Important
CP-3	**demonstrate leadership within the health-care team.**		
a.	collaborate with other members of the health-care team to teach, implement and evaluate care.	CP-3a	Very important
b.	assess, initiate and revise goals and priorities.	CP-3b	Very important
c.	assign and provide clinical guidance to unregulated health workers.	CP-3c	Very important
d.	provide, receive and reflect on constructive feedback.	CP-3d	Important
e.	collaborate with other members of the health-care team to coordinate the actions of others in emergency situations, including fire alarms, codes and disease outbreak.	CP-3e	Important
f.	integrate evidence-informed research in collaboration with members of the health-care team.	CP-3f	Important
g.	participate in quality improvement and risk management activities.	CP-3g	Important

Appendix B

Regulatory Authorities

To obtain information on writing the CPNRE, contact the regulatory authority in your province or territory.

Alberta

College of Licensed Practical Nurses of Alberta
St. Albert Trail Place
13163 – 146 Street
Edmonton AB T5L 4S8
1-800-661-5877 (toll-free in AB)
Tel: 780-484-8886
Fax: 780-484-9069
E-mail: info@clpna.com
Web: www.clpna.com

British Columbia

College of Licensed Practical Nurses of British Columbia
260-3480 Gilmore Way
Burnaby BC V5G 4Y1
1-887-373-2201 (toll-free in BC)
Tel: 778-373-3100
Fax: 778-373-3102
E-mail: exams@clpnbc.org
Web: www.clpnbc.org

Manitoba

College of Licensed Practical Nurses of Manitoba
463 St. Anne's Rd
Winnipeg MB R2M 3C9
1-877-663-1212 (toll-free in MB)
Tel: 204-663-1212
Fax: 204-663-1207
E-mail: info@clpnm.ca
Web: www.clpnm.ca

New Brunswick

Association of New Brunswick Licensed Practical Nurses
384 Smythe Street
Fredericton NB E3B 3E4
1-800-942-0222
Tel: 506-453-0747
Fax: 506-459-0503
Web: www.anblpn.ca

Newfoundland and Labrador

College of Licensed Practical Nurses of Newfoundland and Labrador
9 Paton Street
St. John's NL A1B 4S8
1-888-579-2576 (toll-free in NF)
Tel: 709-579-3843
Fax: 709-579-8268
E-mail: info@clpnnl.ca
Web: www.clpnnl.ca

Northwest Territories

Government of Northwest Territories
Department of Health and Social Services
Centre Square Tower #8
PO Box 1320
Yellowknife NT X1A 2L9
Tel: 867-920-8058
Fax: 867-873-0484

Nova Scotia

College of Licensed Practical Nurses of Nova Scotia
Cogswell Tower, Suite 1212
2000 Barrington Street
Halifax NS B3J 3K1
1-800-718-8517 (toll-free in NS)
Tel: 902-423-8517
Fax: 902-425-6811
E-mail: info@clpnns.ca
Web: www.clpnns.ca

Ontario

College of Nurses of Ontario
101 Davenport Road
Toronto ON M5R 3P1
1-800-387-5526 (toll-free in ON)
Tel: 416-928-0900
Fax: 416-928-6507
E-mail: cno@cnomail.org
Web: www.cno.org

Prince Edward Island

Licensed Practical Nurses Association of Prince Edward Island
PO Box 20058
Charlottetown PE C1E 1E9
Tel: 902-566-1512
Fax: 902-892-6315
E-mail: info@lpna.ca
Web: www.lpna.ca

Saskatchewan

Saskatchewan Association of Licensed Practical Nurses
100-2216 Lorne Street
Regina SK S4P 2M7
1-888-257-2576
Tel: 306-525-1436
Fax: 306-347-7784
E-mail: lpnadmin@salpn.com
Web: www.salpn.com

Yukon

Registrar of Licensed Practical Nurses
Department of Community Services
Consumer Services C-5
PO Box 2703
Whitehorse YT Y1A 2C6
1-800-661-0408 local 5111 (toll-free in the Yukon)
Tel: 867-667-5111
Fax: 867-667-3609
E-mail: consumer@gov.yk.ca

Appendix C

Abbreviations used in the CPNRE and Practice Exam

a.c. - before meals
b.i.d. - twice a day
BMI - body mass index
BP - blood pressure
BUN - blood urea nitrogen
cc - cubic centimetre
cm - centimetre(s)
ECG - electrocardiogram
EEG - electroencephalogram
EENT - ear, eye, nose, throat
G - gram(s)
gtt - drops
h - hour
Hgb - hemoglobin
HIV - Human immunodeficiency virus
HR - heart rate (beats/min)
IM - intramuscular
INR - international normalized ratio
IV - intravenous
kg - kilogram(s)
kJ - kilojoule(s)
mcg - microgram
L - litre(s)
RR - respiratory rate (breaths/min)
stat. - immediately
T - temperature (X °C)
t.i.d. - three times a day
mEq - milliequivalent
mg - milligram(s)
min - minute(s)
mL - millilitre(s)
mmHg - millimetres of mercury
mmol/L - millimole(s) per litre
n.p.o. - nothing by mouth
NSAID - nonsteroidal anti-inflammatory drug
°C - degrees Celsius
P - pulse
p.c. - after meals
pH - hydrogen ion concentration; potential of hydrogen
p.o. - orally, by mouth
p.r.n. - as needed
q.3h - every 3 hours
q.15min - every 15 minutes
q.i.d. - four times a day
R - respiration

Additional Material

Scoring the Practice Exam

Performance Profile Tally Sheet

Table 1			
Competency Category	Total Incorrect	Total in Category	% Incorrect
Professional, ethical and legal practice	÷	37 X	100 = %
Foundations of practice	÷	113 X	100 = %
Collaborative practice	÷	30 X	100 = %

Performance Profile Tally Sheet

Table 2			
Cognitive Levels	Total Incorrect	Total in Category	% Incorrect
Knowledge/comprehension	÷	20 X	100 = %
Application	÷	92 X	100 = %
Critical thinking	÷	68 X	100 = %

Scoring the Practice Exam

Performance Profile Chart

Competency Category																				
% of incorrect answers	0	5	10	15	20	25	30	35	40	45	50	55	60	65	70	75	80	85	90	95
Professional, ethical and legal practice																				
Foundations of practice																				
Collaborative practice																				

Performance Profile Chart

Cognitive Level																				
% of incorrect answers	0	5	10	15	20	25	30	35	40	45	50	55	60	65	70	75	80	85	90	95
Knowledge/ comprehension																				
Application																				
Critical thinking																				

ANSWER SHEET
FEUILLE-RÉPONSES

Family Name - Nom de famille	First Name - Prénom
Writing Centre Code - Code de centre d'examen ___ ___ - ___ ___ ___	
Date of Writing - Date de l'examen DY - JR / MO / YR - AN	
Test - Examen	

PRINT the test form number from the test book cover.

INSCRIVEZ le numéro du formulaire qui apprait sur la couverture du cahier d'examen.

Test Form
Formulaire

Place CANDIDATE LABEL here.

Apposer l'AUTOCOLLANT DU CANDIDATE ici.

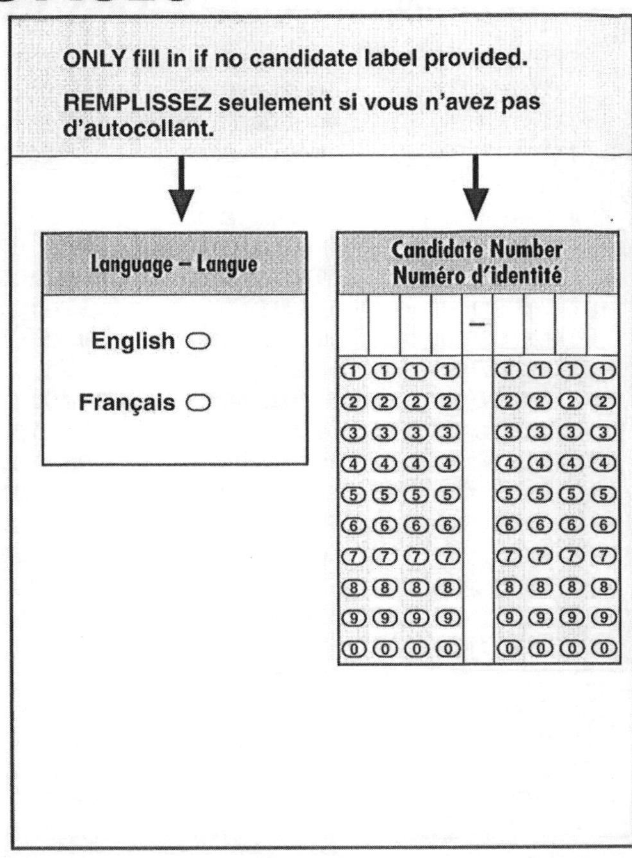

INSTRUCTIONS

- Use a #2 HB pencil.
- Do NOT use ink or ballpoint pens.
- Completely fill the ovals. Failure not to do so may result in no credit.

- Utilisez un crayon HB #2.
- Ne PAS utiliser de stylo.
- Noircissez les ovales complètement, sinon aucun point ne vous sera accordé.

EXAMPLES/EXEMPLES

Right/Correct

Wrong/Incorrect

- Completely erase any answer you wish to change.
- Do NOT make any stray marks on the answer sheet.
- Do not fold or staple the answer sheet.

- Effacez complètement les réponses que vous voulez changer.
- Ne faites AUCUNE autre marque sur la feuille-réponses.
- Ne pas plier ou agrafer la feuille-réponses.

PLEASE CONTINUE WITH ANSWERS ON BACK

TOURNEZ LA PAGE POUR INSCRIRE VOS RÉPONSES

Signature

EXAMINATION QUESTIONS SECTION/SECTION DES QUESTIONS D'EXAMEN

1 ①②③④	43 ①②③④	85 ①②③④	127 ①②③④	169 ①②③④	211 ①②③④
2 ①②③④	44 ①②③④	86 ①②③④	128 ①②③④	170 ①②③④	212 ①②③④
3 ①②③④	45 ①②③④	87 ①②③④	129 ①②③④	171 ①②③④	213 ①②③④
4 ①②③④	46 ①②③④	88 ①②③④	130 ①②③④	172 ①②③④	214 ①②③④
5 ①②③④	47 ①②③④	89 ①②③④	131 ①②③④	173 ①②③④	215 ①②③④
6 ①②③④	48 ①②③④	90 ①②③④	132 ①②③④	174 ①②③④	216 ①②③④
7 ①②③④	49 ①②③④	91 ①②③④	133 ①②③④	175 ①②③④	217 ①②③④
8 ①②③④	50 ①②③④	92 ①②③④	134 ①②③④	176 ①②③④	218 ①②③④
9 ①②③④	51 ①②③④	93 ①②③④	135 ①②③④	177 ①②③④	219 ①②③④
10 ①②③④	52 ①②③④	94 ①②③④	136 ①②③④	178 ①②③④	220 ①②③④
11 ①②③④	53 ①②③④	95 ①②③④	137 ①②③④	179 ①②③④	221 ①②③④
12 ①②③④	54 ①②③④	96 ①②③④	138 ①②③④	180 ①②③④	222 ①②③④
13 ①②③④	55 ①②③④	97 ①②③④	139 ①②③④	181 ①②③④	223 ①②③④
14 ①②③④	56 ①②③④	98 ①②③④	140 ①②③④	182 ①②③④	224 ①②③④
15 ①②③④	57 ①②③④	99 ①②③④	141 ①②③④	183 ①②③④	225 ①②③④
16 ①②③④	58 ①②③④	100 ①②③④	142 ①②③④	184 ①②③④	226 ①②③④
17 ①②③④	59 ①②③④	101 ①②③④	143 ①②③④	185 ①②③④	227 ①②③④
18 ①②③④	60 ①②③④	102 ①②③④	144 ①②③④	186 ①②③④	228 ①②③④
19 ①②③④	61 ①②③④	103 ①②③④	145 ①②③④	187 ①②③④	229 ①②③④
20 ①②③④	62 ①②③④	104 ①②③④	146 ①②③④	188 ①②③④	230 ①②③④
21 ①②③④	63 ①②③④	105 ①②③④	147 ①②③④	189 ①②③④	231 ①②③④
22 ①②③④	64 ①②③④	106 ①②③④	148 ①②③④	190 ①②③④	232 ①②③④
23 ①②③④	65 ①②③④	107 ①②③④	149 ①②③④	191 ①②③④	233 ①②③④
24 ①②③④	66 ①②③④	108 ①②③④	150 ①②③④	192 ①②③④	234 ①②③④
25 ①②③④	67 ①②③④	109 ①②③④	151 ①②③④	193 ①②③④	235 ①②③④
26 ①②③④	68 ①②③④	110 ①②③④	152 ①②③④	194 ①②③④	236 ①②③④
27 ①②③④	69 ①②③④	111 ①②③④	153 ①②③④	195 ①②③④	237 ①②③④
28 ①②③④	70 ①②③④	112 ①②③④	154 ①②③④	196 ①②③④	238 ①②③④
29 ①②③④	71 ①②③④	113 ①②③④	155 ①②③④	197 ①②③④	239 ①②③④
30 ①②③④	72 ①②③④	114 ①②③④	156 ①②③④	198 ①②③④	240 ①②③④
31 ①②③④	73 ①②③④	115 ①②③④	157 ①②③④	199 ①②③④	241 ①②③④
32 ①②③④	74 ①②③④	116 ①②③④	158 ①②③④	200 ①②③④	242 ①②③④
33 ①②③④	75 ①②③④	117 ①②③④	159 ①②③④	201 ①②③④	243 ①②③④
34 ①②③④	76 ①②③④	118 ①②③④	160 ①②③④	202 ①②③④	244 ①②③④
35 ①②③④	77 ①②③④	119 ①②③④	161 ①②③④	203 ①②③④	245 ①②③④
36 ①②③④	78 ①②③④	120 ①②③④	162 ①②③④	204 ①②③④	246 ①②③④
37 ①②③④	79 ①②③④	121 ①②③④	163 ①②③④	205 ①②③④	247 ①②③④
38 ①②③④	80 ①②③④	122 ①②③④	164 ①②③④	206 ①②③④	248 ①②③④
39 ①②③④	81 ①②③④	123 ①②③④	165 ①②③④	207 ①②③④	249 ①②③④
40 ①②③④	82 ①②③④	124 ①②③④	166 ①②③④	208 ①②③④	250 ①②③④
41 ①②③④	83 ①②③④	125 ①②③④	167 ①②③④	209 ①②③④	
42 ①②③④	84 ①②③④	126 ①②③④	168 ①②③④	210 ①②③④	

SURVEY SECTION/SECTION DU SONDAGE

Do not mark examination answers in this section. **N'inscrivez pas vos réponses aux questions d'examen dans cette section.**

1 ⒶⒷⒸⒹⒺ	6 ⒶⒷⒸⒹⒺ	11 ⒶⒷⒸⒹⒺ	16 ⒶⒷⒸⒹⒺ	21 ⒶⒷⒸⒹⒺ
2 ⒶⒷⒸⒹⒺ	7 ⒶⒷⒸⒹⒺ	12 ⒶⒷⒸⒹⒺ	17 ⒶⒷⒸⒹⒺ	22 ⒶⒷⒸⒹⒺ
3 ⒶⒷⒸⒹⒺ	8 ⒶⒷⒸⒹⒺ	13 ⒶⒷⒸⒹⒺ	18 ⒶⒷⒸⒹⒺ	23 ⒶⒷⒸⒹⒺ
4 ⒶⒷⒸⒹⒺ	9 ⒶⒷⒸⒹⒺ	14 ⒶⒷⒸⒹⒺ	19 ⒶⒷⒸⒹⒺ	24 ⒶⒷⒸⒹⒺ
5 ⒶⒷⒸⒹⒺ	10 ⒶⒷⒸⒹⒺ	15 ⒶⒷⒸⒹⒺ	20 ⒶⒷⒸⒹⒺ	25 ⒶⒷⒸⒹⒺ

SCANTRON Mark Reflex® EM-284789-1:654321 HR04 Printed by Vangent Canada Limited. To re-order, call 1-800-665-8774.

ANSWER SHEET
FEUILLE-RÉPONSES

Family Name - Nom de famille First Name - Prénom

Writing Centre Code - Code de centre d'examen

___ ___ - ___ ___ ___

Date of Writing - Date de l'examen

DY - JR / MO / YR - AN

Test - Examen

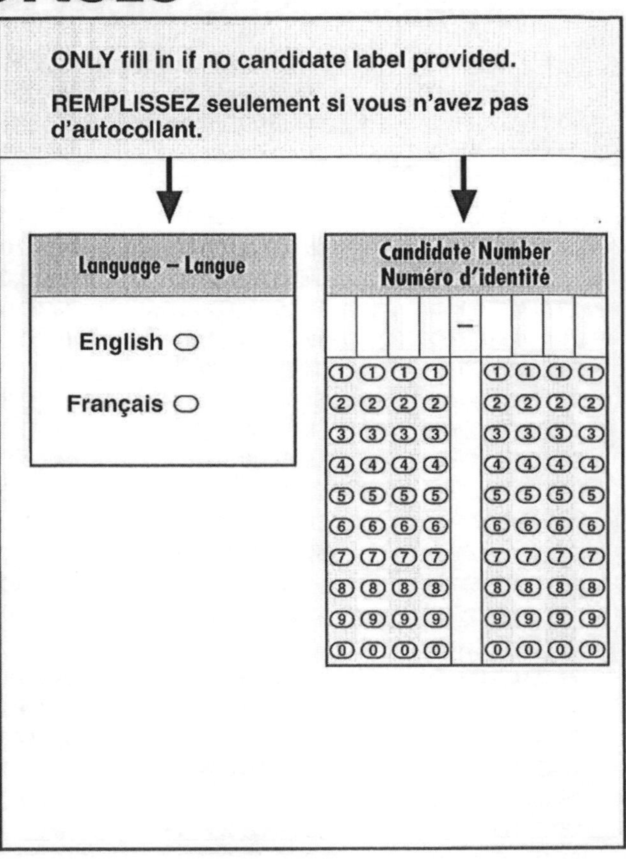

Place CANDIDATE LABEL here.

Apposer l'AUTOCOLLANT DU CANDIDATE ici.

PRINT the test form number from the test book cover.

INSCRIVEZ le numéro du formulaire qui appraît sur la couverture du cahier d'examen.

Test Form
Formulaire

INSTRUCTIONS

- Use a #2 HB pencil.
- Do NOT use ink or ballpoint pens.
- Completely fill the ovals. Failure not to do so may result in no credit.

- Utilisez un crayon HB #2.
- Ne PAS utiliser de stylo.
- Noircissez les ovales complètement, sinon aucun point ne vous sera accordé.

EXAMPLES/EXEMPLES

Right/Correct

Wrong/Incorrect

- Completely erase any answer you wish to change.
- Do NOT make any stray marks on the answer sheet.
- Do not fold or staple the answer sheet.

- Effacez complètement les réponses que vous voulez changer.
- Ne faites AUCUNE autre marque sur la feuille-réponses.
- Ne pas plier ou agrafer la feuille-réponses.

PLEASE CONTINUE WITH ANSWERS ON BACK

TOURNEZ LA PAGE POUR INSCRIRE VOS RÉPONSES

ASI/SEI 04.03

Signature

EXAMINATION QUESTIONS SECTION/SECTION DES QUESTIONS D'EXAMEN

1 ① ② ③ ④
2 ① ② ③ ④
3 ① ② ③ ④
4 ① ② ③ ④
5 ① ② ③ ④
6 ① ② ③ ④
7 ① ② ③ ④
8 ① ② ③ ④
9 ① ② ③ ④
10 ① ② ③ ④
11 ① ② ③ ④
12 ① ② ③ ④
13 ① ② ③ ④
14 ① ② ③ ④
15 ① ② ③ ④
16 ① ② ③ ④
17 ① ② ③ ④
18 ① ② ③ ④
19 ① ② ③ ④
20 ① ② ③ ④
21 ① ② ③ ④
22 ① ② ③ ④
23 ① ② ③ ④
24 ① ② ③ ④
25 ① ② ③ ④
26 ① ② ③ ④
27 ① ② ③ ④
28 ① ② ③ ④
29 ① ② ③ ④
30 ① ② ③ ④
31 ① ② ③ ④
32 ① ② ③ ④
33 ① ② ③ ④
34 ① ② ③ ④
35 ① ② ③ ④
36 ① ② ③ ④
37 ① ② ③ ④
38 ① ② ③ ④
39 ① ② ③ ④
40 ① ② ③ ④
41 ① ② ③ ④
42 ① ② ③ ④
43 ① ② ③ ④
44 ① ② ③ ④
45 ① ② ③ ④
46 ① ② ③ ④
47 ① ② ③ ④
48 ① ② ③ ④
49 ① ② ③ ④
50 ① ② ③ ④
51 ① ② ③ ④
52 ① ② ③ ④
53 ① ② ③ ④
54 ① ② ③ ④
55 ① ② ③ ④
56 ① ② ③ ④
57 ① ② ③ ④
58 ① ② ③ ④
59 ① ② ③ ④
60 ① ② ③ ④
61 ① ② ③ ④
62 ① ② ③ ④
63 ① ② ③ ④
64 ① ② ③ ④
65 ① ② ③ ④
66 ① ② ③ ④
67 ① ② ③ ④
68 ① ② ③ ④
69 ① ② ③ ④
70 ① ② ③ ④
71 ① ② ③ ④
72 ① ② ③ ④
73 ① ② ③ ④
74 ① ② ③ ④
75 ① ② ③ ④
76 ① ② ③ ④
77 ① ② ③ ④
78 ① ② ③ ④
79 ① ② ③ ④
80 ① ② ③ ④
81 ① ② ③ ④
82 ① ② ③ ④
83 ① ② ③ ④
84 ① ② ③ ④
85 ① ② ③ ④
86 ① ② ③ ④
87 ① ② ③ ④
88 ① ② ③ ④
89 ① ② ③ ④
90 ① ② ③ ④
91 ① ② ③ ④
92 ① ② ③ ④
93 ① ② ③ ④
94 ① ② ③ ④
95 ① ② ③ ④
96 ① ② ③ ④
97 ① ② ③ ④
98 ① ② ③ ④
99 ① ② ③ ④
100 ① ② ③ ④
101 ① ② ③ ④
102 ① ② ③ ④
103 ① ② ③ ④
104 ① ② ③ ④
105 ① ② ③ ④
106 ① ② ③ ④
107 ① ② ③ ④
108 ① ② ③ ④
109 ① ② ③ ④
110 ① ② ③ ④
111 ① ② ③ ④
112 ① ② ③ ④
113 ① ② ③ ④
114 ① ② ③ ④
115 ① ② ③ ④
116 ① ② ③ ④
117 ① ② ③ ④
118 ① ② ③ ④
119 ① ② ③ ④
120 ① ② ③ ④
121 ① ② ③ ④
122 ① ② ③ ④
123 ① ② ③ ④
124 ① ② ③ ④
125 ① ② ③ ④
126 ① ② ③ ④
127 ① ② ③ ④
128 ① ② ③ ④
129 ① ② ③ ④
130 ① ② ③ ④
131 ① ② ③ ④
132 ① ② ③ ④
133 ① ② ③ ④
134 ① ② ③ ④
135 ① ② ③ ④
136 ① ② ③ ④
137 ① ② ③ ④
138 ① ② ③ ④
139 ① ② ③ ④
140 ① ② ③ ④
141 ① ② ③ ④
142 ① ② ③ ④
143 ① ② ③ ④
144 ① ② ③ ④
145 ① ② ③ ④
146 ① ② ③ ④
147 ① ② ③ ④
148 ① ② ③ ④
149 ① ② ③ ④
150 ① ② ③ ④
151 ① ② ③ ④
152 ① ② ③ ④
153 ① ② ③ ④
154 ① ② ③ ④
155 ① ② ③ ④
156 ① ② ③ ④
157 ① ② ③ ④
158 ① ② ③ ④
159 ① ② ③ ④
160 ① ② ③ ④
161 ① ② ③ ④
162 ① ② ③ ④
163 ① ② ③ ④
164 ① ② ③ ④
165 ① ② ③ ④
166 ① ② ③ ④
167 ① ② ③ ④
168 ① ② ③ ④
169 ① ② ③ ④
170 ① ② ③ ④
171 ① ② ③ ④
172 ① ② ③ ④
173 ① ② ③ ④
174 ① ② ③ ④
175 ① ② ③ ④
176 ① ② ③ ④
177 ① ② ③ ④
178 ① ② ③ ④
179 ① ② ③ ④
180 ① ② ③ ④
181 ① ② ③ ④
182 ① ② ③ ④
183 ① ② ③ ④
184 ① ② ③ ④
185 ① ② ③ ④
186 ① ② ③ ④
187 ① ② ③ ④
188 ① ② ③ ④
189 ① ② ③ ④
190 ① ② ③ ④
191 ① ② ③ ④
192 ① ② ③ ④
193 ① ② ③ ④
194 ① ② ③ ④
195 ① ② ③ ④
196 ① ② ③ ④
197 ① ② ③ ④
198 ① ② ③ ④
199 ① ② ③ ④
200 ① ② ③ ④
201 ① ② ③ ④
202 ① ② ③ ④
203 ① ② ③ ④
204 ① ② ③ ④
205 ① ② ③ ④
206 ① ② ③ ④
207 ① ② ③ ④
208 ① ② ③ ④
209 ① ② ③ ④
210 ① ② ③ ④
211 ① ② ③ ④
212 ① ② ③ ④
213 ① ② ③ ④
214 ① ② ③ ④
215 ① ② ③ ④
216 ① ② ③ ④
217 ① ② ③ ④
218 ① ② ③ ④
219 ① ② ③ ④
220 ① ② ③ ④
221 ① ② ③ ④
222 ① ② ③ ④
223 ① ② ③ ④
224 ① ② ③ ④
225 ① ② ③ ④
226 ① ② ③ ④
227 ① ② ③ ④
228 ① ② ③ ④
229 ① ② ③ ④
230 ① ② ③ ④
231 ① ② ③ ④
232 ① ② ③ ④
233 ① ② ③ ④
234 ① ② ③ ④
235 ① ② ③ ④
236 ① ② ③ ④
237 ① ② ③ ④
238 ① ② ③ ④
239 ① ② ③ ④
240 ① ② ③ ④
241 ① ② ③ ④
242 ① ② ③ ④
243 ① ② ③ ④
244 ① ② ③ ④
245 ① ② ③ ④
246 ① ② ③ ④
247 ① ② ③ ④
248 ① ② ③ ④
249 ① ② ③ ④
250 ① ② ③ ④

SURVEY SECTION/SECTION DU SONDAGE

Do not mark examination answers in this section. **N'inscrivez pas vos réponses aux questions d'examen dans cette section.**

1 Ⓐ Ⓑ Ⓒ Ⓓ Ⓔ
2 Ⓐ Ⓑ Ⓒ Ⓓ Ⓔ
3 Ⓐ Ⓑ Ⓒ Ⓓ Ⓔ
4 Ⓐ Ⓑ Ⓒ Ⓓ Ⓔ
5 Ⓐ Ⓑ Ⓒ Ⓓ Ⓔ
6 Ⓐ Ⓑ Ⓒ Ⓓ Ⓔ
7 Ⓐ Ⓑ Ⓒ Ⓓ Ⓔ
8 Ⓐ Ⓑ Ⓒ Ⓓ Ⓔ
9 Ⓐ Ⓑ Ⓒ Ⓓ Ⓔ
10 Ⓐ Ⓑ Ⓒ Ⓓ Ⓔ
11 Ⓐ Ⓑ Ⓒ Ⓓ Ⓔ
12 Ⓐ Ⓑ Ⓒ Ⓓ Ⓔ
13 Ⓐ Ⓑ Ⓒ Ⓓ Ⓔ
14 Ⓐ Ⓑ Ⓒ Ⓓ Ⓔ
15 Ⓐ Ⓑ Ⓒ Ⓓ Ⓔ
16 Ⓐ Ⓑ Ⓒ Ⓓ Ⓔ
17 Ⓐ Ⓑ Ⓒ Ⓓ Ⓔ
18 Ⓐ Ⓑ Ⓒ Ⓓ Ⓔ
19 Ⓐ Ⓑ Ⓒ Ⓓ Ⓔ
20 Ⓐ Ⓑ Ⓒ Ⓓ Ⓔ
21 Ⓐ Ⓑ Ⓒ Ⓓ Ⓔ
22 Ⓐ Ⓑ Ⓒ Ⓓ Ⓔ
23 Ⓐ Ⓑ Ⓒ Ⓓ Ⓔ
24 Ⓐ Ⓑ Ⓒ Ⓓ Ⓔ
25 Ⓐ Ⓑ Ⓒ Ⓓ Ⓔ

SCANTRON Mark Reflex® EM-284789-1:654321 HR04

Printed by Vangent Canada Limited. To re-order, call 1-800-665-8774.

Satisfaction Survey – *CPNRE PREP GUIDE*

Your opinion is important to help us improve future editions of *The Canadian Practical Nurse Registration Examination Prep Guide* and to better meet the needs of practical nurse students. Please complete the following questionnaire and mail or fax it to ASI (*see address and fax number at the end of the survey*).

Your responses will be treated with complete confidentiality. Please fill in the circle corresponding to your response.

A: *CPNRE Prep Guide* Content

Please rate the following aspects of the prep guide content.

	Poor	Fair	Average	Good	Excellent
1. Background on the CPNRE	O	O	O	O	O
2. Test-taking strategies	O	O	O	O	O
3. Practice Exam	O	O	O	O	O
4. Score interpretation of the Practice Exam	O	O	O	O	O
5. Performance Profiles	O	O	O	O	O
6. Answer rationales	O	O	O	O	O
7. Classification of questions (in Rationales and Performance Profiles)	O	O	O	O	O
8. References	O	O	O	O	O
9. Overall content of the prep guide	O	O	O	O	O
10. Overall usefulness of the prep guide in helping you prepare for the CPNRE	O	O	O	O	O
11. CD-ROM	O	O	O	O	O

Comments/Suggestions: ______________________________

B: *CPNRE Prep Guide* Format

Please rate the following aspects of the prep guide format:

	Poor	Fair	Average	Good	Excellent
1. Overall size and length of the prep guide	O	O	O	O	O
2. Type of binding	O	O	O	O	O
3. Organization/layout of the prep guide	O	O	O	O	O
4. Ease of use of CD-ROM	O	O	O	O	O
5. Colour/graphics of CD-ROM	O	O	O	O	O

Comments/Suggestions: ______________________________

____

____

____

____

____

C: *CPNRE Prep Guide* Marketing

1. How did you hear about the prep guide?
   - O Poster/advertisement
   - O Other practical nurse student
   - O Brochure
   - O Conference
   - O Practical Nurse faculty
   - O Website
   - O Other ______________________________

2. Where did you purchase the prep guide?
   - O School Book Store
   - O ASI's distribution centre
   - O Other ______________________________

3. How much did you pay for the prep guide, including taxes?
   - O $84.95
   - O Other ______________________________

   Do you think this is reasonable?
   - O Yes
   - O No

4. Did you use any other exam book(s) in addition to the *CPNRE Prep Guide?*
   - O Yes
   - O No

   If yes, which did you prefer?
   - O The *CPNRE Prep Guide*
   - O Other (please specify) ______________________

5. What do you plan to do with your copy of the prep guide after you have written the CPNRE?
   - O Keep it
   - O Give it away
   - O Sell it
   - O Other ______________________

6. Did you use the CD-ROM?
   - O Yes
   - O No

7. Who are you?
   - O Student
   - O Instructor
   - O Other (please specify) ______________________

D: General Comments

____

____

____

____

____

____

____

____

____

____

Thank You for Completing This Survey

Please send this completed survey by mail to:

Canada's Testing Company, Assessment Strategies Inc.
1400 Blair Place, Suite 210, Ottawa ON K1J 9B8

by fax to: 613-237-6684
or pdf to corporate@asinc.ca